THE POWER OF THE MACHINE

For the first time in history, technology has become not merely one of the many threads that form the texture of our civilization, but its determining agent. The sciences, the arts, politics, education, war, the way we make our livings, the way we live, all are vitally influenced by the machine—for good or for ill.

In this important, thought-provoking book, R. J. Forbes charts the contrast between previous epochs and our own. He studies the forces at work within the evolution of technology that have made the rate and direction of its development more and more unresponsive to human needs. And he vividly presents the choices that may spell the difference between a future man-made paradise or machine-made hell.

ABOUT THE AUTHOR: *R. J. Forbes,* a member of the Royal Netherlands Academy of Sciences and Secretary of the Dutch Society of Sciences at Haarlem, was Professor of the History of Science and Technology at the University of Amsterdam from 1947 to 1967. He served as an International Council of Scientific Unions observer on the UNESCO Commission for a History of the Scientific and Cultural Development of Mankind and has written extensively on the history and archaeology of technology. Among his many works are *Man the Maker, Studies in Early Petroleum History*, and the nine-volume *Studies in Ancient Technology.*

Other Britannica Perspectives
in MENTOR Editions

($1.25 each)

THE LEARNING SOCIETY by Robert M. Hutchins. (#MY926)

MAN AND THE COSMOS: The Nature of Science Today by Ritchie Calder. (#MY927)

PROGRESS AND DISILLUSION: The Dialects of Modern Society by Raymond Aron. (#MY928)

ANATOMY OF THE LAW by Lon L. Fuller. (#MY933)

THE LABYRINTH OF LANGUAGE by Max Black. (#MY934)

RELIGION IN A SECULAR AGE: The Search for Final Meaning by John Cogley. (#MY941)

MAN, MEDICINE, AND ENVIRONMENT by Rene Dubos. (#MY942)

MATHEMATICS AND LOGIC: Retrospect and Prospects. (#MY944)

ART, AFFLUENCE AND ALIENATION: The Fine Arts Today by Roy McMullen. (#MY945)

The Conquest of Nature

Technology and Its Consequences

by R. J. Forbes

MENTOR

A MENTOR BOOK

Published by
THE NEW AMERICAN LIBRARY,
New York and Toronto

For information address Frederick A. Praeger, Publishers,
111 Fourth Avenue, New York, New York 10003.

Library of Congress Catalog Card Number: 68-28157

This is an authorized reprint of a hardcover edition
published by Frederick A. Praeger, Publishers.

THE CONQUEST OF NATURE: TECHNOLOGY AND ITS CONSEQUENCES is a *Britannica Perspective* prepared to commemorate the 200th anniversary of *Encyclopaedia Britannica*.

MENTOR BOOKS are published *in the United States* by
The New American Library, Inc.,
1301 Avenue of the Americas, New York, New York 10019,
in Canada by The New American Library of Canada Limited,
295 King Street East, Toronto 2, Ontario

FIRST PRINTING, SEPTEMBER, 1969

PRINTED IN THE UNITED STATES OF AMERICA

Acknowledgments

THE PROBLEM OF this study was first dealt with at the *Encyclopædia Britannica* Conference convened at Santa Barbara, Calif., in March, 1962, in connection with the *Britannica Perspectives* series. The point of departure was a background paper prepared for that occasion by Jacques Ellul of the University of Bordeaux, who had touched off an international discussion with the radical view of contemporary manifestations of technology in his *La Technique* (Paris, 1954; also published as *The Technological Society*, Knopf, 1964). Among the participants at Santa Barbara were:

Lord Ritchie-Calder, University of Edinburgh
W. Norris Clarke, S.J., Fordham University
Arthur Goldschmidt, Department of Economic and Social Affairs, United Nations
William Gorman, Center for the Study of Democratic Institutions
A. Rupert Hall, University of Indiana
Willy Hartner, University of Frankfurt
Aldous Huxley, Author
Melvin Kranzberg, Case Institute of Technology
Richard L. Meier, University of Michigan
Walter Ong, S.J., Wesleyan University
Gerard Piel, Publisher, *Scientific American*
James Real, Center for the Study of Democratic Institutions
Vu Van Thai, United Nations
Robert Theobald, Author
Ralph W. Tyler, Director, Center for Advanced Study in the Behavioral Sciences
Sir Robert Watson-Watt, Scientist and Author
Lynn White, Jr., University of California at Los Angeles
John Wilkinson, University of California at Santa Barbara
A. Zvorikine, U.S.S.R. Academy of Sciences

The proceedings of the Conference, edited by Carl F. Stover for the Board of Editors of *Encyclopædia Britannica*, were published in the fall 1962 issue of *Technology and Culture*, the international quarterly of the Society for the History of Technology (also as *The Technological Order*, Wayne State University Press, 1963). Additional unpublished background papers were prepared by Mr. Stover, Warren E. Preece, the present Editor in Chief of the *Encyclopædia Britannica*, and by J. Bronowski, the distinguished British technologist and author. The issues of the technological order also were on the agenda at the *Encyclopædia Britannica* Conference on Science held in Florence, Italy, in June 1964.

There is, of course, no implication of agreement with the views of this author in his grateful acknowledgment of the debt he owes to those who have participated in this extensive background preparation. Some supplementary language has been provided in the final reorganization of the author's manuscript by Harry S. Ashmore, Editor of the series, and Elisabeth Mann Borgese.

Preface

THE EDITOR AND PUBLISHER of *Scientific American,* Gerard Piel, has written of the world's most advanced technological society:

> Because the time lag between invention and application now diminishes so swiftly, it becomes possible–and necessary—to forecast the ethical, social and economic implications of this development. Today, in our country and in certain other industrial nations, men are compelled to recognize and give assent to profound transformations in human values. Technological change has already largely eliminated people from production; it has sundered the hitherto socially essential connection of work to consumption . . . .

U Thant, Secretary-General of the United Nations, addressing himself to the global implications of the new Western technology, has said:

> The truth, the central stupendous truth, about developed countries today is that they can have—in anything but the shortest run—the kind and scale of resources they decide to have. . . . It is no longer resources that limit decisions. It is the decision that makes the resources. This is the fundamental revolutionary change—perhaps the most revolutionary mankind has ever known.

Thus we have come to the time when it is proper to speak of a technological order, and already many people do so, often with fear and trepidation. Technology can no longer be viewed as only one of many threads that form the texture of our civilization; with a rush, in less than half a century, it has become the prime source of material change and so determines the pattern of the total social fabric.

In its earlier phases there was no serious question of the governance of technology by *Homo faber* and *Homo ludens;* this continued to be the case during the slow growth of the craft tradition, evolving intermittently as individual master craftsmen were moved by necessity and inspiration to improve their product. The motivating impulses came from the desires and needs of the societies they served, and limitations were set by the quality and quantity of raw materials available to them. Only three centuries ago, in the time of Bacon, the scientist's theoretical knowledge of nature came to be joined effectively with the trial-and-error skills of the craftsmen. The machine-dominated environment of the West dates from that fateful juncture.

Basic Distinctions

Simpler, limited definitions of technology still survive. The *Oxford English Dictionary* sees technology as "the scientific study of the practical or industrial arts," and *Webster's Third New International Dictionary* calls it "the science of the application of knowledge to practical purposes" and "the totality of the means employed by a people to provide itself with the objects of material culture."

Contemporary usage, however, constantly pushes the definition of technology beyond these limits. Max Salvadori offers this: "Technology is the daughter of science, which applies the fundamental truths of science to the solution of particular problems of physical, biological or economic problems." Under the Marxist definition of A. Zvorikine, technology is the work within a social system of production including "all the material conditions necessary to enable the production process to take place at all," and "the means . . . of human activity developing within a system of social production and social life."

The ultimate definition may be that offered by Jacques Ellul in *The Technological Society*. Ellul holds "la technique" to be "the ensemble of forces by which one uses available resources in order to achieve certain valued ends"—a definition from the American, Harold Lasswell. Here "technique" is more nearly equivalent to the technological order than it is to technology in the conventional sense. This closed system, as Ellul sees it, is now responding to its own imperative and threatens to exclude man from any effective degree of control:

> It is possible, if the human being falters even momentarily in accommodating himself to the technological imperative, that he will be excluded from it completely even in his mechanical functions, much as he finds himself excluded from any participation in an automated factory.[1]

The citation of a technological imperative almost always comes, as it does here, from one who views technology from the outside. Few practitioners in the field would accept Ellul's dire view. Sir Robert Watson-Watt, the "father of radar," does not believe the definition of technology can be taken beyond "the mechanism of man's needs to his ends." Lynn White, Jr., a leading historian of science, holds technology to embrace "the systematic modification of the physical environment for human ends." Both abstain from claiming that these ends should be preconceived or material. Much of our modern machinery evolved out of the age-old effort to relieve man of onerous physical burdens and provide the leisure the spirit requires; though the means were undoubtedly material the end was not. Nor have technologists and inventors always confined themselves to well-defined projects; until recent years much change came about through random discovery and inadvertent application.

This paper accepts as its working definition of technology the mental or physical activity by which man alone, or together with his fellowmen, deliberately tries to change or manipulate his environment. He may be acting on the ground of empirical or theoretical knowledge, or he may be simply following a hunch. Since there is a technological component in virtually every overt action of man, there also may be an impulse, subconscious rather than well conceived, to outdo or better this component. We would not be *Homo faber* if we did not act that way.

..[1] Jacques Ellul, translated by John Wilkinson, Alfred A. Knopf, Inc., New York, 1964.

The Technological Order

The technological order is the cultural complex that results from technology and technological acts. It does not always bear close relation to its technical origins, and it includes a host of nontechnical presuppositions. Technological acts are accepted, wherever found, if they somehow harmonize with all other technological acts so as to permit an intelligent ordering of their totality. In the technological order the technological act is supported by recognizable intellectual, procedural, and institutional contexts.

Acceptance of the act may be based on recognition of its true technical values, but very often it is prompted by impulses which are not of a scientific or technical nature at all. Such an impulse may derive from the simple idea, which seems to be shared by many of our fellowmen, that it is desirable to have more and more things. The acceptance of technological acts and their insertion into the technological order depends therefore on their importance to mankind in general rather than upon their impact upon individual men. This may be the reason why the individual may consider himself adversely affected by the technological order, which may contradict what he believes he stands for in life.

The Environmental Imperative

The technological order has been with us since man became *Homo faber*. At least since prehistoric times it has been sufficiently important in quality and quantity to constitute a major element of every society's way of life. Now the technological order and technology must be understood in a new, pervasive sense if we are to comprehend the world we live in and the world that is emerging. Werner Heisenberg writes in *Das Naturbild der heutigen Physik* (1955) that "many of our technical apparatuses will perhaps in the future belong as inescapably to man as the snail's shell does to the snail and the spider's web to the spider," and adds that "the apparatus would then be rather a part of our human organism." This leads him to the conclusion that "technology can be considered as a large-scale biological process," as he put it in *Physik und Philosophie* (1959). Insofar as it helps to shape man's environment, technology may be considered, from the biologist's point of view, as the instrument with which man seeks to gain an increasingly firm grip on his own evolution.

The assumption that every technological act carries within itself further possibilities and applications is often interpreted in a fatalistic way. Man is, and has always been, part of his environment. He could not exist apart from it. At all times and under all circumstances there has been an environmental imperative which man could not ignore. Technology, then, is the product of interaction between man and environment, based on the wide range of real or imagined needs and desires which guided man in his conquest of Nature. There were always a few men who could, by a deliberate act of will, abstain from acting and lead an ascetic life wholly conditioned by Nature. But for most humans every technological act involves further possibilities of development and application in his struggle with his environment. That struggle is not over, and may, indeed, have only begun.

Every technological act disperses the favourable or unfavourable arguments that may have preceded its realization. History seems to teach that we cannot go back upon technological decisions. We may steer and guide a technological act, but retrograde movements like that of the Luddites, who rebelled against the machines in the 19th century, are doomed to failure. For "man is at the mercy of man," and all of us, not only the technologists, are responsible for the search for new technologies and for the exploration of possibilities a technological act has revealed.

Technology has taken different courses in different countries, depending upon the consensus as to the demands and aspirations of the society. The Chinese culture once blocked the mechanization of trades by forbidding use of the windmill and the waterwheel their craftsmen had developed. But the very same machines were the ancestors of the prime movers of the Western world, and these became the core of modern machine-dominated society. In each case technology received a different external impulse, and in each culture the response to the environmental imperative was significantly different.

The Technologist's Standard

The technologist's own standard is one of efficiency; seeking proper means to a defined end, he can evaluate the result only in terms of technical success or failure. The selection of the ends, on the other hand, and their evaluation in terms of their ultimate social impact, lies beyond the technological act. It is because of this that technology can be described as self-propagating only in the limited sense that one technological act may permit or even require another. But in modern times the applied research that produces groups of interrelated technological acts is most often the product of a larger general design set in response to nontechnological goals.

The author of this work finds no iron chain of causes and effects leading up to our modern milieu. Neither the great proliferation of technology, its variety, its complex role in modern life, nor the stress we lay on certain technologies and their products, can be explained by any theory of "self-generation." There is a constant interchange between technological achievements and human values; in many of his technical productions man has embodied his beliefs and his aspirations without bothering about the process or the practical consequences. The results have been baleful and benign; technology has produced cathedrals and nuclear bombs.

Because the great political and ideological tensions of our time are related inescapably to the impact of technical change, there is a tendency to view the history of technological development solely in terms of its end product. But the fact is that the modern vocabulary rapidly loses meaning as we proceed into the past. Contemporary terms like "progress," "mechanization," "efficiency," "proletariat," and even "factory" were not relevant until comparatively recent years. They cannot be applied without producing a gravely distorted picture of the roots of modern technology. And this in turn often produces an equally distorted view of the aims and prospects of the technological order.

No serious man can doubt the perils of the new age of technology, and not even the fatuous any longer expect the laboratory to produce automatically ready answers to the problems raised by technologists as they exploit secrets of Nature that scientists have unlocked. A solemn injunction has been offered by one who stands near the professional summit; Professor Dennis Gabor of the Imperial College of Science and Technology, London, said:

> . . . exponential curves grow to infinity only in mathematics. In the physical world they either turn round and saturate, or they break down catastrophically. It is our duty as thinking men to do our best towards a gentle saturation, instead of sustaining the exponential growth, though this faces us with very unfamiliar and distasteful problems.

The Presentation

This work is an effort to treat in ordinary language the principles and trends of the technological order, and to examine their interaction with the other great forces of the modern age. It is divided into three parts devoted to the reciprocal relations between Man, Machine, and Milieu.

The first part deals at some length with Man and Machine, and traces the evolution of the main elements of the technological order. The second is addressed to Machine and Milieu, and to the changes wrought in man's environment by the advent of the new technology. The final part examines the interactions between Milieu and Man. The hope is that these three perspectives will illuminate the great issues raised by the emerging machine-dominated and automatized world, a place of promise and danger, where man must confront in new ways his ancient problem of remaining human in the face of his own creations.

Contents

PART ONE

MAN AND MACHINE

THE AIM OF TECHNOLOGY has always been the extension and improvement of material culture by the observation and use of natural objects, phenomena, and forces. Civilization began with man's first attempt to convert into artifacts the materials he found in Nature. The first craftsmen had come to grips with man's environment and were making great utilitarian contributions to society long before science began to consider the welfare of mankind the principal object of the study of Nature. But whatever its aims and methods, technology always has been limited by Nature; for the greater part of our history material change was narrowly confined by the elementary natural "laws" identified by the early scientists.

It was against these limits that man directed his centuries-old effort to create *machines*, instruments which partly or wholly eliminated the necessity of expending his own manual labour on the work required to provide the necessities and amenities of life. When he finally succeeded in getting Nature to do his work, man had created a prime mover, and had launched a new historical epoch that would shortly outstrip all the technological achievements back to the dawn of time.

The record of human achievements during the millennia is the story of an ever increasing concentration of energy expended on materials to be shaped, transformed, and transported. The primary test of technology, then, has always been its efficiency in processing available materials; it was in this effort that the technologist learned to harness the forces of Nature and put them to his service. In this never ending enterprise *Homo sapiens*, Man the Thinker, appears also as the toolmaker, *Homo faber*. Discovery and invention were the product of his dreams of a better life.

Homo Faber

Technology begins with man, the first toolmaking primate. The earliest Hominidae, who roamed the earth some twenty-five million years ago, may have made tools, although the evidence they left behind was too scattered by their ceaseless migrations to be conclusive. But at least by the time of Peking man, about half a million years ago, man had learned to select stones for his special purposes, and to shape them by percussion against other stones.

Lower animals also use a stone now and then to break a shell, or employ a stick as an aid in carrying out some of their feeding or breeding habits. But none of these animals, not even primates, use tools in the sense that man does—that is, as the usual way of coping with unusual situations. Man's monopoly on toolmaking is undoubtedly connected with the advanced functional anatomy of the human hand. The muscles in the hands of monkeys do not differ much from those of early men, but the nervous mechanism by which the latter were able to direct the movements of these muscles seems to have been of a finer structure, making human hands more flexible and responsive than those of other primates.

Thus toolmaking is related to the larger and more efficiently organized cerebrum of man, the centre of intelligence and functional control that led him to grope for improvements on the hands and teeth with which he confronted Nature. The first toolmakers were carnivorous and needed stabbing and cutting edges; as their world became more differentiated, tools of special types emerged for use in hunting or fishing, and then for providing shelter and clothing. From Peking man forward, archaeologists are able to identify and classify the basic characteristics of early human settlements according to the shape and the type of the tools always found with human remains.

As the earliest eoliths were superseded by shaped stones, a number of more or less standardized shapes emerged as chopper tools and pointed flakes. About 100,000 years ago came pear-shaped hand axes, scrapers, knives, and the like. By 15,000 B.C., flint, obsidian, and fine-grained lava provided materials which could be shaped into a good cutting ax. Gradually there emerged a wide range of special artifacts for chopping, cutting, adzing, and sawing. It is noteworthy that the cutting angle of these tools is practically identical with that of their modern steel descendants.

By the beginning of the Neolithic Age, man had at his disposal an arsenal of specialized tools. His efficiency improved as he learned to select denser and harder stones and to shape them by grinding and polishing. The search for the necessary stones led to the beginnings of mining and to the first vestiges of trade. In the earlier stages tribesmen probably organized seasonal excursions to find and select suitable stones, and during the Neolithic Age flint mining (and perhaps the fashioning of flint tools on the spot) may have reached the estate of man's first craft.

Homo Sapiens

The earliest toolmaking efforts were accompanied and guided by the development of speech. The visual impression of animals seems to be a totality, whereas man has the apparently unique ability to leave this mythical whole behind and differentiate between the objects of his senses. The evolution of speech is the sure indication of the growth of such diversity in the human world. "And whatsoever Adam called every living creature, that was the name thereof. And Adam gave names to all cattle, and to the fowl of the air, and to every beast of the field." Genesis 2:19-20). The immense importance of the disintegration of total vision into a number of disparate pictures of things, with their inner relations forming the patterns of man's world, can be appreciated if one remembers the sudden rapture of the blind, deaf-mute Helen Keller when she discovered that "everything had a name."

Speech and language fully joined *Homo faber*, the toolmaking man, and *Homo sapiens*, the thinking man. Not only did his ability to design specialized artifacts demonstrate that his mental activity was of a different order from that of other primates but from now on he was to be engaged in producing technological extensions of his body in various forms. From early times his interest was attracted not only to terrestrial objects but to celestial phenomena; both turn up among the drawings and sketches on the walls of his cave dwellings. These sketches can be said to represent the rudiments of science, as they also served as practical aids to the craftsman. Man's mind can be seen to be developing in these ancient records of the clear ordering of his observations and the intelligent characterization of the objects he observed.

Then, as now, two elements governed man's technical progress: discovery and invention. Discovery, the recognition and careful observation of natural objects and phenomena, is highly subjective until it leads to practical application, either directly or indirectly. Discovery represents the disintegration of part of the total world picture through the observation and classification of its components. Invention is a mental process through which various discoveries and observations are combined and, guided by experience, result in a new tool or process. Hence invention is the result of often very slow accretion of small details. It is the product of an evolution, somewhat resembling a biological process, which eventually leads to the flash of insight in the inventor's mind fitting together all the pieces of the puzzle.

Invention can rarely be attributed to one man only; it is ordinarily the product of a long chain of acts, and the rate at which these are undertaken may be determined by the material needs and spiritual limitations of the world in which the inventor lives, as well as by his personal powers. Great inventions are often foreshadowed by the "dreamers of the world," the spiritual leaders of civilization, who set the standards of their time. And it is quite correct to reverse the aphorism and say that invention can also be the mother of necessity; cause and effect work both ways.

Inventions appeared slowly and erratically in prehistoric and preclassical times. With the birth of agriculture in the Near East around 8000 B.C., man needed new tools to separate grain from the chaff of the wild grasses he cultivated and crossed. He found a simple solution by beating sheaves of grain against a compact mud threshing floor, and improved upon this by spreading the grain on the floor and beating it with sticks. Later, animals were used to tread on the grain or to drag a threshing sledge studded with flint or metal nails. These crude methods continued with little change through the time of the Romans, whose large estates evolved mass production of wheat and other cereals. The Romans managed to invent, among other things, a kind of mechanical reaper, the *plostellum poenicum*. But so simple a tool as the ingenious flail, consisting of two hinged sticks, did not appear until 4th-century Gaul.

Progress in material culture was slow in those times, furthermore, because discoveries and inventions could not be diffused rapidly. Traders, prospectors, and wandering craftsmen carried technical knowledge with them, but even the most obvious advances were often slow in gaining wide acceptance. It is becoming increasingly clear from early documents that this sporadic spread of ideas and techniques was not wholly a matter of primitive communications. The resistance to early discoveries and inventions varied greatly, and was rooted in the fundamental structure of the various civilizations. Spiritual values and tenets often deterred material achievement long after technical knowledge was readily available—and still do.

Fire and Its Implications

Primitive man, alarmed and threatened by forest fires, at last turned danger into a boon. At first he could not replace the precious flames he took from Nature, and so he performed his first great technological act; Paleolithic man in Asia and Europe devised a method of striking lumps of flint against pyrites to produce a spark to light tinder, and in the jungle areas where stones were not accessible, tools were developed to produce heat by friction with two pieces of wood. The control of fire literally transformed the early cultures.

The use of heat in the preparation of food greatly enhanced the previous diet of raw meat, fruit, and roots; now man could "predigest" other foodstuffs, and could dry meat and fish to tide him over the lean seasons. The increase of carbohydrates in his diet led to the collection and mining of salt, needed to make up for the deficiency of natural salt in these new foodstuffs. The art of cooking gradually extended beyond open-flame roasting, broiling, and grilling to the use of preheated stones and glowing embers. As suitable containers evolved, boiling, stewing, and frying became possible. These advances in the means of satisfying man's appetite led to a chain of technical achievements: need for a convenient place for the fire produced a primitive mud-plastered hearth; development of portable fires such as braziers were the beginning of domestic heating; grates, fans, and bellows came into being to make fires more dependable and efficient—and our modern furnaces are in the direct line of descent.

Industrial processes such as metallurgy, pottery-making, and brewing turned to account the accumulated experience of prehistoric cooks. In all early languages such operations as heating, drying, steaming, baking, and washing are referred to by the terms used in the kitchen. Even so late a growth as alchemy, which can hardly date back further than the 8th century B.C., employed not only the terminology but the apparatus; filters and water baths are original kitchen equipment adapted for chemical operations.

It is important to realize that for centuries the *fuel* used remained of the most primitive kind. Shrubs, twigs, dried grass, and dung were the common source of heat. Therefore, until well into classical times, all operations requiring heating were expensive, and baked bricks, for example, were used for ceremonial buildings only. The best fuel available was charcoal, which could be had only in wooded regions, and in Egyptian technology its use was avoided unless it was imperative. Coal was known early, but could only be used locally. This natural limitation on the fuel supply severely restricted technological development and shaped the patterns of developing civilizations until well into the 18th century. It was, indeed, the need for charcoal, along with shipbuilding and the grazing of goats in the arid hilly districts, that resulted in the substantial deforestation of the Mediterranean region, a fact of which Plato took note.

Fire also provided the first form of lighting. Resinous splinters and torches were the beginning, but were soon ousted by the more efficient and stable lamps burning fish oil or other fats. The advent of the wax candle came before the Christian era, providing greater convenience but no real improvement in the quality of lighting. And so until very recent years the day was divided by the availability of natural light; people got up and went to bed with the sun, since study or work during the evenings was difficult if not impossible.

The Urban Evolution

For many centuries prehistoric man subsided as a forager, hunter, and fisher, and his condition was reflected in the kinds of tools and weapons he developed. During the Neolithic Age, he became a stockbreeder and farmer, and his technology both produced and adapted to the change. The Egyptians are known to have tamed and bred gazelles and antelopes to obtain leather prepared from their skins, and in this pattern other animals were domesticated. Agriculture began with the cultivation of wild grasses, and later their selection and crossing, in the highlands to the north of the Fertile Crescent and in Syria. By the beginning of the historic period (3500 B.C.) the valuable naked wheats, such as durum, had been developed out of the wild grasses which are the ancestors of our modern cereals.

Stockbreeding and agriculture stabilized life by concentrating an abundant food supply and permitting the roaming tribes to settle down. This new sedentary pattern emerging in the early farming communities around 8000 B.C. had a profound influence on technology. The processing of meat and cereals, the dressing of skins, and the building of suitable houses and stables provided impulses for the development of many new tools. The hoe, the plow, and the harrow appeared. Soon man was cultivating plants for purposes other than food. Flax and hemp provided fibres for textiles and ropemaking, and it was found that there were plants from which oils and dyestuffs could be extracted.

During the Neolithic Age markedly different ways of life developed in the Mediterranean coastal areas, the northern forest areas, the high-latitude grasslands, and in the Arctic regions, where a hunting economy has survived to the present day. In every region a technology evolved suited to the local economy and environment, and out of this came the material hallmarks that differentiated the several cultures.

So far as we know, there existed neither specialization nor division of labour in these early societies. The situation changed, however, when the early farming communities in the Near East began to develop into urban centres, as in the case of Jericho, which had attained city status by 6000 B.C. Stockbreeding and farming had been refined to a point where it produced a "social surplus," as Gordon Childe has called it, and this bounty made urbanization possible. The fertile region that supported the city could afford to trade surplus foodstuffs for products which were available beyond, in the hilly and mountainous countries. Mining, metallurgy, and pottery may have developed as the first full-time specialized occupations, as men in the mountainous regions converted the natural materials found there into products to exchange for scarce foodstuffs.

A regional trade in mass products, such as edible oils (mainly olive oil), cereals, and wine, developed between the rural districts and the cities. The urbanites included not only the officials of government and the priests and their assistants but also specialized craftsmen. In combination, these city dwellers produced the great civilizations of the Nile, the twin rivers Euphrates and Tigris, the Indus, and the Yellow River. As the higher steppe regions that are now the Sahara and the Arabian and Central Iranian deserts began to grow arid about 8000 B.C., the early farmers moved into the river valleys, which had to be drained and cultivated. Here they did not readily find the ores and stone which they had used for making their tools, and hence the rise of miners and smiths as the first craftsmen produced by the emerging urban society.

The world of these early craftsmen was dominated by irrigation farming, dependent upon the rising rivers and the silt they carried down the mountains. In Egypt and in Mesopotamia (where the Sumerians reigned until the Assyrians and Babylonians took over around 2000 B.C.) the social order and the technology bore the strong imprint of religious and philosophical concepts produced by these special conditions. With the invention of writing (3500 B.C.) this spiritual world of the ancients opens to us. It is not insignificant that the earliest documents we know are concerned with administrative matters of the material society although they were prepared under priestly aegis; these are clay tablets used in Mesopotamian temples to record the incoming and outgoing goods of the temple storehouses.

The interrelation between the evolution of speech and of toolmaking is evident in those early documents, which bear witness to the tremendous impression the "naming of things" must have made on early men. All natural things and phenomena were registered in word lists (onomasticons) in which terms referring to animals, plants, minerals, stars, etc., are arranged in groups supposed to have something in common. These lists form the basis for "ordering the things in nature," and were essential to the budding scientist. The craftsman used the same terminology to record his experience and to formulate directions and instructions for the technical operations he was gradually developing.

Both in Egypt and in Mesopotamia the only education was provided by the school attached to the temple. Here aspiring clerks, officials, and priests learned to read and write and were exposed to the knowledge required for the office of scribe, which was highly honoured by society. There is no doubt that in these schools the pupils were taught the "order of things as established by the gods in the beginning," with the aid of word lists. Some of the mathematics taught in these schools dealt with very practical problems involving the conversion of standard measures or weights and calculation of the areas and volumes of various geometrical figures and solids, *e.g.*, the volume of earth needed to build a dike of a certain section and length or the area of a given piece of land. Thus out of the temples came technicians who rose to the high estate of officials surveying great engineering works or responsible for the production or import of essential goods.

Apart from this, technical products were often submitted for inspection and advice to learned persons of priestly rank. There were actually advisory boards for this purpose in various towns in Egypt (the "Houses of Life") and in Mesopotamia ("House of Mummu"). The first great public buildings and monuments had religious aspects, and the boards were called upon to pass judgment on the plans for such structures.

The Creative Act

There is much evidence of the force of the spiritual world which motivated and limited the early technologist. Religious requirements governed his choice of the limited possibilities inherent in the materials at his disposal. The Egyptian sculptor was much more skilled than his Mesopotamian contemporary, who had only limited access to stone which had to be imported from the mountainous regions at great expense and trouble. However, the form of the final product in either case was limited by convention and particularly by the ritual use for which statues were often made. The Egyptian term for sculptor was "he who makes alive." His statue had to conform to certain religious precepts in order to be endowed with magical potency by the "Ritual of the Opening of the Mouth" performed by the priests, and to serve as the body into which the soul of the departed was to descend to communicate with the world of the living. Sketches on potsherds demonstrate that the painters who decorated the burial places were able to make realistic drawings, but convention required the stylized tomb paintings when performed as a duty for the dead.

This blend of religion and technology can be traced in crafts such as metallurgy and glassmaking. It was generally believed that Nature had its own way of producing metals and ores which "grew" in the bowels of the earth. When plying his craft, the smith was therefore interfering with natural processes. The gods of spirits who guided his work had to be propitiated by offerings and prayers; the smith had to be ritually clean when exercising his craft, and he had to pay heed to many taboos. The craftsmen, who thus took over "acts of creation" from the gods, were regarded with awe and sometimes even honoured as magicians. This reverence extended to their tools; one has but to recall the place the smith's hammer takes in many legends and that an oath sworn over the anvil was held to be particularly binding. A Sumerian poem extols the divine origin and virtues of various tools. And there are Assyrian texts commanding the glassmaker to bury a fetus underneath a new furnace and to say propitiatory prayers before lighting it. The satyr's mask on the Greek potter's kiln had a magical function.

There is evidence that the craftsmen themselves attached supernatural significance to the creative act by which they shaped their materials. Certainly they often worked in the spirit of artists, and their hands and tools produced things which we still admire because they display a beauty beyond the call of utility.

The First Factories

Technology in preclassical and classical antiquity was characterized by the small workshop. The Latin *fabrica* was nothing but the place of the *faber*, a smith or worker in hard materials. The ordinary establishment was run by a single craftsman who might have one or two slaves to assist him in producing goods on a modest scale. Although slavery was common in the *fabricas* of classical times, it was not an economic success in the trades. Slavery was generally found on a commercial scale only in agricultural or mining undertakings, and even here ancient agronomists were already warning that it was an expensive type of labour which paid only if employed full time in a combination of agriculture and horticulture (vineyards, vegetables, and orchards). The modest level of affluence in the *fabricas* is shown by inventories of many ancient workshops which indicate that apart from their tools the craftsmen possessed only a few household goods.

The dominant characteristic of ancient technology is the lack of machinery. There were no prime movers designed to activate other machines and thereby replace manual labour. The early technologists had to get along with the energy that could be provided by harnessing human or animal power. The limitation did not preclude erecting massive monuments and public buildings, but this required masses of labourers; the cranes used by the Romans for the heaviest lifting were operated by treadles moved by human feet.

The Great Pyramid of King Khufu (Cheops), built around 2500 B.C., is perhaps the classic illustration of monumental results achieved without even the aid of pulleys or tackles. The Pyramid consists of some 2,300,000 blocks of limestone, weighing about four tons each. The joints were chiseled on the spot, no mortar was used, and the exterior was finished with slabs of polished granite brought down from Aswan. The limestone blocks were quarried on the other bank of the Nile, ferried across the river, and hauled onto the pyramid plateau above the Nile Valley. From there, temporary earthen ramps (which finally had as large a volume as the entire pyramid) were built to the building level. The skilled masons and quarrymen were paid craftsmen, but transport duties were performed by statute labour, that is, a vast army of peasants paying their taxes in sweat during the period of inundation when farming was impossible. The building of an entire city of temporary huts to house the workmen, and the organization required to remove debris, to supply materials and tools, and to feed the people (up to 100,000, according to Herodotus) resulted in the emergence of a new managerial class of "organizers," as mentioned in the texts.

The remains of the two great aqueducts of the Assyrian kings and those of the Greco-Roman cities also testify to great engineering feats performed despite the lack of prime movers. In many cases it was the Roman army's peacetime mission to provide or organize the labour for such work, notably road building. These projects were either financed by the state or made possible by the munificence of private citizens who wanted to demonstrate their public spirit.

Tools and Machines

The classical craftsmen had much better tools at their disposal than their ancestors of the Pyramid Age. Preclassical technology was the manifestation of the copper and bronze tools that finally ousted prehistoric stone tools, although the Egyptian army continued to use flint arrowheads until iron became available around 400 B.C., because flint had better penetrative power than copper or bronze. By 1000 B.C. nearly all tools were made of copper and bronze, the use of the latter being limited by the scarcity of tin in the Near East.

Bronze was tougher, made finer edges possible, and produced tools much more durable, malleable, and fusible than those of the stone age. The metal was also much more expensive, and hence bronze sickles, hoe blades, and hammerheads came into common use relatively late. Bronze is sometimes called "the metal of aristocracy" in contrast with iron, "the metal of democracy." Iron ores were fairly abundant in nearly all countries in antiquity, and the diffusion of smelting and working techniques made iron the dominant metal of Greco-Roman times. Many bronze tools continued in use, however, since the proper quenching and tempering techniques for the production of surface-steeled wrought iron remained difficult to apply until the early centuries of our era. By the 6th century B.C. the coming of iron made possible the advent of tongs, frame saws, and the lathe, and two centuries later hinged compasses and true paired shears were known. Still later came metal-bladed scythes, spades, and other agricultural tools, the plane, the auger, nail-heading anvils, and draw-blocks for wire.

The scarcity of prime movers did not indicate a general lack of ingenuity among the early engineers. They had developed water-raising machinery which could be driven by oxen, and the lighter Archimedean screw to be turned by hand or foot. This machinery was used not only for irrigation but to drain mines in Spain and elsewhere. Rotary motion had been applied to crushing machinery and adapted to the donkey mills that supplied flour for Greek and Roman bakeries and to the roller mill (*trapetum*) used for crushing olives and other agricultural products. Then there were the beam press, the screw press, and the wedge press with their variants, serving agriculture, viniculture, and the pharmaceutical and perfume industries. The handbooks of Hero of Alexandria (Heron) and other classical engineers show that they were well versed in the design and construction of large and sophisticated pieces of machinery. Throughout this period the science of mechanics was beginning to direct its attention to the laws governing such devices as the lever, the pulley, the windlass, the wedge, and the screw, and was even dealing mathematically with the motion of falling and projected bodies. But, apart from some general basic principles, science provided little help for the technologists who were constructing increasingly complex machinery.

The classical engineers made a great breakthrough when they turned their attention to the possibilities of the water wheel, discovered by the Greeks of the mountainous regions of the Near East. The first model was a small wooden water turbine directly coupled to a set of millstones. The Roman engineers of the 1st century B.C. overcame the initial limitations of this primitive construction by placing the water wheel in a vertical position and gearing the shaft of the wheel to create the horizontal or Vitruvian mill. Thus was created a prime mover with an output of some three horsepower, the possibilities of which can be appreciated by comparing it with the 0.4 horsepower output of the old water turbine and the 0.5 horsepower required to move the best type of donkey mill for grinding grain. Like all later prime movers, the new *hydromula* was put to use in mass production, the only such industry then existing being the grinding of grain. No other application of the water-driven prime mover is known until after the fall of the Roman Empire. The number of *hydromulae* did not increase significantly until the 3rd century A.D., when there was an acute shortage of labour, and an overflow of water from one of Rome's aqueducts was available to move the wheels.

Geographical conditions in the Mediterranean region did not favour the erection of such expensive machinery. Most rivers carried widely varying quantities of water in different seasons so that the wheels would stand idle during part of the year unless they could be fed by a constant flow from a costly aqueduct. About A.D. 310 aqueducts were specially constructed to drive two sets of eight undershot water wheels built on the slope of a hill near Arles, which at that time was the "flour factory" for the army of southern Gaul, and a similar set of wheels at Tournus which provided for the northern army. A water mill was built in 5th-century Athens, when the town was declining and a surplus of water could be taken from the aqueduct leading to the *agora*.

These cases, however, were exceptional and, generally speaking, vested interests held out against the introduction of this kind of machinery even in towns as large as Rome, where its use certainly would have been economically justified. Here the structure of the ancient economy played a restrictive role. The only goods produced and transported on any substantial scale were cereals, wine, and olive oil, and to a certain extent pottery, which provided the containers in which these products were shipped and stored. But even this packing material par excellence of antiquity came from small workshops or at most from *egasteria,* which were not factories in the present sense but establishments like the ateliers of the 18th century where many craftsmen assembled under one roof to produce goods from materials supplied by the wealthy owner of the building. When the buildings were owned by the craftsmen themselves they ordinarily did not turn their profits to account by investing in new tools or machinery, and systematic expansion was rare. Practically all other products of the crafts were made for local use on a small scale in shops where power-driven machinery would not have been economically feasible.

The Scientific Method

The Roman Empire was an agglomeration of autarkic production areas which did not suffer from sharp economic crises or from overproduction. Capital was invested in slaves and land, not in costly machinery, since labour was cheap enough in a society that provided bare necessities for the masses and a few luxuries for the elite. Many Romans thought that technology had already fulfilled its task with the limited applications of their time, and this complacency may have contributed to the fall of the Roman Empire.

There was no real interplay between science and technology. The Greeks called the scientist a "philosopher," from which came the term "natural philosophy" applied to science until recent years. Sometimes these philosophers were called *physiologoi,* those who investigated "the natural growth of things," but they always devoted their research to *theoria; praxis* did not interest them, for practical concerns would not have helped to support their philosophical theories. The *technitae* (craftsmen) were looked down upon; they had no time to devote their *otium* (leisure) to things of the mind as did the intelligent patricians. They had to carry out their *negotium,* and "sitting indoors like women" was presumed to kill the philosophical spirit in the class among whom even physicians were reckoned. When Archimedes deigned to construct machinery to defend his besieged hometown, Syracuse, Plutarch excused him by calling such machinery "the byproducts of a jesting geometry." He noted firmly that the construction of engines and, in general, any trade exercised for its practical value is base.

This gulf between science and the crafts was not bridged by the Romans, even though practical engineering was held in greater esteem and was employed by the central government to establish and maintain its hold on the riches of the Empire. It must not be forgotten that ancient science could have given the craftsmen little help in any event. The philosopher had a clear understanding of the scientific method, but his results were mainly qualitative and of no use to the engineer. This continued to be the case, even though a positive appeal for assistance was often made by the craftsmen, who were aware that only limited technical progress was possible without science. In A.D. 320 Pappus of Alexandria wrote in the introduction to the 8th Book of his *Collections:*

> The mechanicians of Heron's school say that mechanics can be divided into a theoretical and a manual part; the theoretical part is composed of geometry, arithmetic, construction, astronomy, and physics; the manual, of work in metals, construction work, carpentering, and the art of painting, and the manual execution of these things. The man who has been trained from his youth in the aforesaid arts and in addition has a versatile mind, will be, they say, the best builder and inventor of mechanical devices. When it is not possible for the same man to excel in so many academic studies, they advise one who wishes to undertake "mechanical work" (*artes mechanicae*) to use such crafts as he already possesses in the tasks to be performed in each particular case.

The superior craftsmen and engineers are called *mechanikos, architektones, tektones,* and *technitæ* in late-Roman and Byzantine texts, the first corresponding more or less to our mechanical engineer; the second was a master builder. But no ancient scientist could have taught them the applied mechanics they needed, for this critical body of theory was not to emerge until the 18th century.

In the 4th century A.D., Ammianus (*c.* 330–after 391) related the decline of the Empire to the lack of interest in science and technology among the Roman leaders: "Accordingly, among their retainers the crooner has replaced the philosopher, the teacher of histrionics that of oratory; they seal their libraries like tombs but construct for themselves hydraulic organs." And the author of *De Rebus Bellicis,* whose inventions intended to save manpower in the army were rejected (about A.D. 370), pointed to the younger nations, the barbarians, who showed marked inventiveness: "in fact this is a quality which we see granted without respect of persons; for although the barbarian peoples derive no power from eloquence and no illustrious rank from office, yet they are by no means considered strangers to mechanical inventiveness, where nature comes to their assistance."

A significant change in attitude came with the conversion of many leading Romans to Christianity. This provided a radically different background against which the science and technology of the future were to develop. The poor had formerly been treated as victims of the gods, often punished for reasons unknown to other men, but the Stoics preached the brotherhood of man and asked mankind to cultivate *philanthropia* and *humanitas* toward their poor and weak brethren. The new Christian concept, *caritas,* implied more than mere friendliness and hospitality; a new attitude toward the poor and the slaves was inherent in the Christian proclamation of the dignity of all work, including manual labour. Slavery would persist for many centuries, but this new view required that the free craftsman be given an honoured position in society, and all diligent workers of any estate accorded respect.

"Be fruitful, and multiply, and replenish the earth, and subdue it," was a Christian command (Genesis 1:28) which implied the possibility of man's conquest of nature. This can be seen as radically different from the prevailing belief of the Ancients that Nature is animate. In the earliest science there was a strong undercurrent of animism which was revived with the rise of Neoplatonism. The nymphs and river gods were not mere poetic conceits, but were very real to the masses in antiquity. Christianity at one stroke did away with this world of animate spirits, and by stripping Nature of its supernatural halo, opened the door to the rational use of natural forces which was to produce the rapidly advancing technology of the Middle Ages.

Power Technology

The fall of the Roman Empire and the recasting of Western Europe, the great invasions, the menace of Islam, and the raids of the Vikings subjected technology to the general stagnation that marked the transitional centuries. However, the lessons of the ancient craftsmen were not forgotten, and they contributed much to the new surge of technical achievement that came as prime movers were introduced on a large scale in a more settled Europe during the 10th to 12th centuries. Here again, as several centuries before, the first notable advances were in agriculture. This is emphasized by Lynn White, Jr., in *Medieval Technology and Social Change:*

> . . . the change of the gravitational center of Europe from south to north is to be found in the agricultural revolution of the early Middle Ages. By the early ninth century all the major interlocking elements of this revolution had been developed: the heavy plough, the open fields, the modern harness, the triennial rotation—everything except the nailed horseshoe, which appears a hundred years later. [It was a major stimulus to the north even in the days of Charlemagne, but it was limited] to the northern plains where the heavy plough was appropriate to the rich soils, where the summer rains permitted a large spring planting, and where the oats of the summer crop supported the horses to pull the heavy plough. It was on those plains that the distinctive features both of the late medieval and of the modern worlds developed. The increased returns from the labour of the northern peasant raised his standard of living and consequently his ability to buy manufactured goods. It provided surplus food which, from the tenth century on, permitted rapid urbanization. In the new cities there arose a class of skilled artisans and merchants, the burghers who speedily got control of their communities and created a novel and characteristic way of life, democratic capitalism. And in this new en-

vironment germinated the dominant feature of the modern world: power technology.[1]

The great power sources of the Middle Ages were the water wheel and the windmill. The latter was a Western design unknown to the ancients, but it was probably inspired by the typical Eastern windmill, which the Crusaders certainly saw. The Western windmill probably appeared in the 12th century, and soon became the typical prime mover of the windy, low plains extending from eastern England via the Low Countries and northern Germany into Latvia and Russia. The earliest mills were used to grind grain, but about a century after they had reached the Low Countries (about A.D. 1300) they were being employed to drain the marshes and to pump accumulating water from the low, drained polders, and this was to be their main task in the centuries to come.

The water wheel was already in service in Western Europe as a prime mover before the first windmills were built. By A.D. 600 *hydromulae* existed in the neighbourhood of Geneva, Dyon, and Angers. The 11th and 12th centuries saw the rapid spread of the hydraulic prime mover through the hills and mountainous regions of Europe where natural conditions were propitious for its propagation, as they were not in the Mediterranean area, or the coastal lowlands of Europe.

The Order of Cistercian Monks, those indefatigable reclaimers of wastelands, played an important role in the diffusion of the water wheel. In the abbeys of Fontenay and Royaumont hydraulic power drove fulling mills, grain mills, and hammer mills in the 13th century. The monks applied the prime mover to iron metallurgy, not only in France but also in Germany, Denmark, and Great Britain; Cistercians and their tenants operated twenty-five out of the thirty hammer forges mentioned in 12th-century French documents. Some of their abbeys had water-wheel powered workshops in which several crafts were plied under one roof.

In Britain there was a similar spectacular increase in the number of water wheels. The earliest charter for a grain mill was granted by Aethelberht of Kent in 762 to the owners of a monastic mill situated east of Dover. By 1086, *Domesday Book* mentions no fewer than 5,624 water mills in 3,000 communities south of the Trent and the Severn.

[1] The Clarendon Press, Oxford, 1962, pp. 76–77.

This mechanization of flour production introduced the miller into these regions, and, via Chaucer, into literature. The water wheels were sources of profit to those who erected them on their land, and hence a mill was annexed to every manor which had a stream to turn it—about one-third of those noted in the *Domesday Book*.

By this time the water wheel not only ground grain but it was widely used as a real prime mover for activating other machinery. *Domesday Book* mentions stamping mills (for crushing ores) and hammer mills. By the 14th century every village of moderate size had a mill of the new type, rented by its miller from the manorial lord. Conflicts between lord and tenant over these commercial arrangements began to play an important role in legal documents.

Hand- or foot-fulling was replaced by fulling with water-driven hammers, and some people claimed that machine fulling did not produce first-class cloth, a complaint that would echo across the centuries as handcrafts gave way to machines. In Central Europe powerful water-driven hammer forges and bellows made possible the new blast furnace process which yielded large masses of cast iron for the first time. Water power opened up silver- and copper-mining on a large scale in the Alpine regions and Scandinavia in the 16th century. The hydraulic prime mover provided a means for drawing metal wire and was harnessed to machinery for drilling gun barrels.

A fulling mill on the Serchio probably made the first application of the cam in machinery in 983, and during the 11th and 12th centuries the discovery was applied to a great variety of operations. Thirteenth-century technicians discovered the practical value of the spring and the treadle; in the 14th, gearing developed to levels of incredible complexity; in the 15th, elaboration of the crank, the connecting rod, and the governor vastly facilitated the conversion of reciprocating machinery to continuous motion and vice versa—a most fertile source of further mechanical development. Indeed, in the four centuries after Leonardo da Vinci—*i.e.*, until electric energy demanded a supplementary set of devices—the technicians were less engaged in seeking new basic principles for their machinery than they were in elaborating and refining the discoveries of the four centuries before Leonardo. The expansion of Europe, beginning with the discovery of the New World, was actually based on Europe's high consumption of energy in the expanding applications of technology, which engendered productivity and economic and military power.

Craft, Capital, and Science

As regional and international trade developed, the city guilds slowly evolved from associations of individual craftsmen into trade unions that had to cope with the growing mechanization of their crafts. The growing demand for their goods and the lack of personal capital gradually forced the craftsmen to yield control of their production to financiers who were acquainted with foreign markets and had access to the necessary raw materials through international trade channels. The process was expedited by the fact that the new machinery which stepped up production was generally too expensive for the individual craftsman. Thus the merchants and bankers who rose to power as feudal society disintegrated drove the crafts toward a new division of labour: "manufacture," the often uneasy partnership between labour and capital which led to the workshops and mills of later centuries and finally to modern factories. The guilds, though still paying much attention to the number and the practical education of their apprentices, gradually left the regulation of the quality of their final products and marketing restrictions to the local authorities.

The crafts tended to split up into more and more guilds, each concerned with only a part of the specialized operations involved in conversion of raw material into the final product. This subdivision and mechanization of industrial processes was very evident in the textile industry, where fulling, dyeing, and finishing came to be undertaken under the aegis of the financing merchant. This sort of external financing and organization began in Flanders during the 13th century and was common in Italy a century later, where no fewer than sixteen guilds were involved in the cycle of production. A similar division of labour grew up in the salt industry and in mining and metallurgy.

Cooperation between science and technology was closer than in earlier times. The medieval scientists, unlike their predecessors of the classical period, were very much aware of the crafts, although they were still unable to apply much of their knowledge to them. Hugo of Saint-Victor (1096-1141) in *Didascalion* considers "mechanics" to be one of the four main subjects to be studied, and the designation included the scientific aspects of the manufacture of textiles, clothing and armament, navigation, agriculture, hunting, medicine, and of the organization and preparation of theatrical shows and spectacles. The practical aspects of these crafts, however, were ruled out because they "are not natural but imitate nature." Ramon Llull in *Arbor Scientiae* (1296) also draws attention to the scientific background of the crafts, which he declares to be worth studying.

By the middle of the 13th century, Lynn White tells us, a considerable group of active minds, stimulated by the technological success of recent generations and in pursuit of the will-o'-the-wisp of perpetual motion, was beginning to generalize the concept of mechanical power and to think of the cosmos as a vast reservoir of energies to be tapped and used according to human requirements. They were power-conscious to the point of fantasy, but without their far-ranging dreams the technology of the Western world would never have developed.

Peter de Maricourt's friend Roger Bacon wrote in 1260: "Machines may be made by which the largest ships, with only one steering them, will be moved faster than if they were filled with rowers; waggons may be built which will move with incredible speed and without the aid of beasts; flying machines can be constructed in which a man may beat the air with wings like a bird; machines will make it possible to go to the bottom of seas and rivers." Bacon spoke for the engineers of his age. Comparable visions show up in the notebooks of Leonardo da Vinci and his contemporaries and in the first technical handbooks.

Technology in Print

Before the coming of the printing press the craftsman derived little guidance from written works. Manuscripts on medieval arts and crafts are rare. We have the 8th-century *Mappae Clavicula* and the *Compositiones ad tigenda musica,* the 10th-century work by Heraclius, and Theophilus' 12th-century work *On Divers Arts,* but these discuss mainly such arts and crafts as the monks needed to build and decorate their churches. These manuscripts, copied by hand, remained beyond the reach of the common craftsman. Neither could he study such interesting documents as Villard de Honnecourt's sketchbook (1245) which, like Leonardo's notebooks, contained drawings of many engines. Written instruction and data on the ways in which others practised their craft became available only when the first stream of printed technical handbooks began to flow during the first half of the 16th century.

The earliest of these, Jacques Besson's *Theatre of Instruments* (1582), or those written by Ramelli (1588), Fausto Veranzio (1595), Branca (1629), and Zonca (1607), display an evident connection with the arts and crafts of the classical period. The new works on metallurgy, mining, and chemical technology by Biringuccio (1540), Agricola (1556), Ercker (1574), and Lohneiss (1617) are in similar vein. Throughout the centuries classical tradition survived among craftsmen, although various new processes were invented and many older ones were improved or adapted; when print became available to them, the new technologists relied upon copious quotations from classical authors to prove that they were right in their choice of the methods recommended. Great ingenuity was displayed by these authors in overcoming technical difficulties without the support of any scientific theory or formula. In some cases they even tried their hand at applied mechanics. Simon Stevin in his essay on windmills attempted to apply the laws of mechanics to the calculation of the output of his mills, but failed because he neglected to allow for the effects of friction in his machinery and the losses of energy thus incurred (1580).

A new age was rapidly dawning. Great figures like Leonardo da Vinci conducted experiments to discover the laws of applied mechanics and obtain a more solid foundation for the engineering projects they advocated, and science in general gradually began to pay attention to technical problems. The Italian academies of the 15th and 16th centuries had begun to discuss such matters, but it was an Englishman who became the prophet of the new era of cooperation between science and technology.

Francis Bacon (1561-1626), of whom Harvey said that "he wrote philosophy [*i.e.*, science] like a Lord Chancellor," not only advocated experimental science instead of purely intellectual and philosophical discussions of natural phenomena; he also stressed the value for science of a study of the "trades," and vice versa. His "Salomon's House" was to be an institute for organized scientific cooperation between scholars in close contact with artisans and manual workers, from whom the scholars might receive many useful suggestions rising from practical experience. Scientific methods were to make the crafts more efficient, and this was to benefit mankind as a whole. The conditions of living would be improved for all, diseases combated, suffering alleviated, and life lengthened. Under prescribed methods, lists of experiments and facts were to be compiled from questionnaires; one example is the "History of Trades" which the Bacon-inspired Royal Society later attempted.

Bacon proclaimed: "The end of our foundation is the knowledge of causes and the secret of things, and the enlarging of the bounds of human empire to the effecting of all things possible." Those words had a tremendous effect upon his generation. Descartes and Huygens, though aware of the one-sidedness of Bacon's experimental method, agreed with him that "true understanding means understanding the causes" and that by diligently pursuing the course set out by Bacon all men would become "*maîtres et possesseurs de la nature.*"

Bacon was justly referred to as "the bell which called the wits together," and through his teachings the Royal Society came into being in 1660. Its charter not only set its Fellows to investigate new patents but also specified a program of practical applications of science, such as the search for an engine to drain mines, which became one of the factors leading to the discovery of a practical steam engine. The *Philosophical Transactions* of the Society contain many reports on investigations of technical matters such as dyeing, the making of better candles, the ventilation of prisons, etc. In France the Académie des Sciences (1666), which was dominated far more thoroughly by the Crown than its British predecessor, was often ordered by Richelieu and his successors to give advice on practical state projects.

Prelude to Revolution

The Industrial Revolution that followed upon this scientific ferment was by no means as sudden as is often claimed, nor as revolutionary as some have believed. It had its roots in the important technological changes of the 16th century, although it did not gain momentum until about 1800. From a social point of view, however, the changes during the period from 1730 to 1880, dramatic in their strange medley of good and evil, often tragic in their combination of material progress and social suffering, might indeed be described as revolutionary.

The primary economic cause was the remarkable expansion of overseas trade in the 17th and 18th centuries. The new markets came first, and the inventions followed, for unconsciously the successful inventors worked within the limits laid down for them by the changing needs of society. The Industrial Revolution first gained momentum in the British Isles with the rise of the industries of Scotland and the Midlands. This was due to a variety of factors. Great Britain had conquered the seas and established the largest overseas markets of all European powers; she had accumulated the capital necessary for industrial experiments and protected it with a stable currency based on gold, an efficient banking system, and a high degree of internal political and social stability. To this were added the natural advantages of abundant iron ore and coal, water power, and a humid atmosphere suitable for the manufacture of textiles. Finally, a substantial number of well-placed Britons were keenly interested in science and scientific experiments.

Thus the economic urge was met and fulfilled by the development of a science and technology which for a time was to set the standard for the world. France followed quite closely. Germany, being politically divided, entered the industrial stage only about 1860-70, by which time the Industrial Revolution had reached the rapidly expanding United States. The new age was in full flower throughout the West by the turn of the century.

The science of mechanics was gradually yielding a better understanding of how machines worked. Attempts at applied mechanics, particularly in testing materials, contributed notably to the development of a variety of practical machines and to the design of well-built engines to move them. But A. P. Usher reminds us that "these developments may seem to be little more than diffusion of knowledge already attained. For a long time, no additional theoretical knowledge would have been of much practical use. It would be an error, however, to minimize the magnitude of the technological changes that opened up the first extensive applications of power. It was the beginning of an essentially new stage in mechanical technique." [2] Adam Smith comments that the great improvement in the engineering arts in the 18th century was due to "the ingenuity of those who are called philosophers or men of speculation, whose trade it is not to do anything but to observe everything, and who, on that account, are often capable of combining together the powers of the most distant and dissimilar objects."

The *amateurs* and *virtuosi* to whom Smith here refers typify a great outburst of lay interest in science and its applications. They found a rallying call in Newton's *Principia,* the *Mathematical Principles of Natural Philosophy* (1687). Newton, having developed the mathematics and mechanics to deal with his subject, the structure of the "Heavenly Clockwork," found in astronomy a multitude of properly verified scientific observations which permitted a synthesis that would not have been possible in any other field of physics at that time. Although the work is written in a lucid and beautiful style, it cannot be considered easy reading even today. But intelligent laymen like Voltaire and Richard Bentley were able to grasp its essentials, and comment on them in popular language so successfully that the original soon became a best seller, going through eighteen reprints within a century.

Within a generation or two after Newton's *Principia,* a number of "learned societies" came into being, such as the Lunar Society of Birmingham (1766), the Literary and Philosophical Society (Manchester, 1781), the Hollandsche Maatschappij der Wetenschappen (Haarlem, 1752), and Teyler's Stichting (Haarlem, 1778). In contrast to most social customs of the time, ladies often took

[2] *A History of Mechanical Inventions,* Harvard University Press, Cambridge, Mass., 1954, pp. 54–55.

part in the meetings and discussions of these bodies and even formed special circles and groups for the study of science.

These "Scientific Societies of Laymen" performed a threefold function. By inviting scientists to lecture they provided instruction in natural science for their members. By collecting natural objects and instruments in their "cabinets" and libraries, they promoted independent study of natural science by the membership, and by offering money rewards for prize essays (often on technological and engineering problems) and financing scientific journals, they advanced research and the dissemination of its results. By admitting scientists as co-members, they fostered a permanent contact between scientists and laymen to the benefit of both. The founders of these societies were mainly bankers, merchants, lawyers, engineers, officials, and gentry. Thus an important segment of the leadership in the lower nobility and the upper middle class were fully converted to a faith in experimental science which they hoped to apply to the arts and crafts in which they were commercially interested.

New Prime Movers

The increasing tendency to substitute machines for hand tools soon demonstrated the grave limitations of the existing power sources, the water wheel and the windmill. Wind was cheap but unreliable; water power was strictly limited by conditions of place. And so the inventors turned to steam, which suffers none of these disadvantages. The invention of the steam engine must be regarded as the crucial fact of the Industrial Revolution. Steam power could be produced on the precise spot where it was wanted and in the desired amount. This new mobility of concentrated energy is the characteristic feature of the new Machine Age, and it made possible the industrialization of many countries otherwise fated to a pastoral existence by deficiencies of wind or water power.

In the early phase of the Industrial Revolution windmills still dotted the landscape. Water remained the main source of power of 18th-century England; the new textile machinery came into being in an area of hills, valleys, and streams, because the early mills had to be built on the banks of the rivers that provided the motive force. The first steam engines were used to pump water back onto the wheel when the natural flow failed or became inadequate. But they were not to remain long a mere accessory. Watt solved the problem of converting the oscillating motion of the engine's beam into rotary motion, and great new possibilities opened up for the noisy new prime mover.

The steam engine depended on the supply of coal, and this quickly became the essential fuel of the Industrial Revolution. By 1600 timber scarcity threatened British metal production, which until then had been a "charcoal industry," as was the German version. Sweden, with rich supplies of both iron ore and timber won many markets during the period when its competitors had to shift to coal and encountered difficulties in finding an adequate substitute for charcoal. For many industries in the south of Britain the imports of "sea coale" from Newcastle solved the problem, but metallurgy could not work its blast furnaces without a hard smokeless form of carbon capable of supporting the masses of ore in the furnace. After many attempts Abraham Darby succeeded in producing the first good metallurgical coke (1717) from anthracite coal. This entailed the transfer of the metallurgical industry to the Midlands, where water power and coke were more readily available. There it also found the new steam engine, as improved by Watt, which was able to crush ores and drive bellows and hammers. By 1800 the Midland coal pits also relied heavily on steam engines for the draining of their shafts, though this meant major capital investment, the cost of installation of a Newcomen engine then being about £1,500.

However, several factors combined to prevent the steam engine from rapidly ousting its competitors. The efforts of early machine builders were seriously handicapped by a lack of skilled workmen. There had never been a guild of metalworkers of the kind they needed, and the first engines were built by a medley of blacksmiths, wheelwrights, and carpenters. The designs of the earlier engines reflect this condition, and only too often the parts refused to work after they were put together. Watt found that cylinders made by the best workmen available in Glasgow varied by ⅜ of an inch in diameter, and Smeaton told him that "neither tools nor workmen existed that could manufacture so complex a machine with sufficient precision." John Wilkinson, however, found ways to tool metal with a limit of error "not exceeding the thickness of a thin sixpence" in a diameter of 72 inches. While the tools for working and measuring metals with such precision were still being developed, Watt had to avoid the use of high steam pressure, which he understood was necessary to achieve a higher thermal efficiency and energy output. Thus the men who grasped the new principle had to train specialists and devise tools to finish machine parts properly before they could put it fully into practice. This was the main task of Watt, Boulton, and their generation.

By 1800, when Watt's patent expired, 496 of his engines had been installed in Great Britain in mines, metal plants, textile factories, and breweries. One or two of these were rated at 40 hp., but the average power was only 15–16 hp. and therefore not significantly higher than that of their water- or wind-driven competitors. The big breakthrough came in the period from 1800 to 1850. Trial and error provided the means for constructing high-pressure engines and for improving the transmission of energy from engine to machine.

Only gradually did several branches of science come to contribute to a more scientific approach to the steam engine: applied mechanics, the science of bridge building, methods devised to measure elasticity and stresses acting on metal, the study of friction, and the elaboration of the theory of gases. The fundamental factor was the development of the theory of heat, which produced calorimetry for temperature measurement and permitted, above all, the development of thermodynamics around 1850. There is truth in L. J. Henderson's statement that "until 1850 the steam engine did more for science than science did for the steam engine." The recognition of the value of energy and its laws for the calculation of steam engines forms the great divide between the old and the new engineering.

Some figures will illustrate the progress of the steam engine in the early 19th century. By 1820 Birmingham counted 60 engines with "1,000 total steam power in horses." In 1835 Lancashire and the West Riding district of Yorkshire had 1,369 steam engines and 866 water wheels. The steam engines had an average of only 15 hp. This rate of progress is reflected in the output of coal in Great Britain, which in 1700 was about 3 million tons (largely used to heat the homes of 6 to 7 million people). This figure had doubled by 1800, owing to coke metallurgy and the introduction of the steam engine. It reached 60 million tons in 1850, a convincing proof that the steam engine by then dominated technology. Even in 1824 Sadi Carnot was right in saying: "To rob Britain of her steam engines today would be to rob her of her coal and iron, to deprive her of the sources of her wealth, to ruin her prosperity, to annihilate that colossal power." By 1850, 40-hp. engines were fairly common, and in special cases steam engines of up to 135 hp., in one case even of 260 hp., were built. In Prussia the average engine of 1835 was 31.5 hp., which figure increased to 55 hp. by 1904.

The New Skills

Training for technology owed little to the universities, for as late as 1800 even science itself was still frowned upon in academic circles. In France natural philosophy found its place only because the strong centralized government began to undertake public works on a large scale during the 17th and 18th centuries. The lack of properly trained experts capable of supervising such works was soon evident. The title "engineer" had been first used in the sense of "architect," but later it came to denote "military engineer," the official charged with building fortresses and other military works. These specialists were professionalized by creation of the *Corps des Ponts et Chaussées* (1716). In 1747 the new profession was broadened beyond the military when the École des Ponts et Chaussées was established; the first engineering school in Europe, it was followed by the École des Mines, and the famous École Polytechnique (1794). The graduates who came from these schools were called *ingénieur civil,* a title they maintain to this day. Their task was defined in the Charter of the Institution of Civil Engineers (1828) as "the art of directing the great sources of power in nature for the use and convenience of man, as means of production and traffic in States, both for the external and internal trade, as applied in the construction of roads, bridges, aqueducts, canals, river navigation, and docks for internal exchange and intercourse, and in the construction of ports, harbours, moles, breakwaters, and lighthouses, and in the art of navigation by artificial power for the purpose of commerce, and in the construction and adaptation of machinery, and in the drainage of cities and towns." Even though mechanical engineering, shipbuilding, and navigation would subsequently be spun off as separate specialties, this imposing charge for civil engineering can be said to be the beginning of professionalization for the technologist.

Such technical education came late to Great Britain, and great engineers like Telford and McAdam were not specially trained for the tasks to which their genius directed them; those with the mechanical bent still had to apprentice with established practitioners. A number of technical colleges grew out of the earlier, rather primitive mechanics' institutes; but the universities entered the field hesitantly. The University of Glasgow had the first chair of engineering, but for a long period the course was not considered to be an examination subject. London followed in 1841, and then Edinburgh (1855). In the United States engineering as an academic discipline was introduced at the University of Michigan (1853), Cooper Union (1859), and the Massachusetts Institute of Technology (1861). The Netherlands had their technical school at Delft (1864), Switzerland at Zürich. By 1860 various towns in Germany had established Polytechnische Schulen and Technische Hochschulen to cope with the demand for trained engineers and technologists for the growing industry in that country. The American Society of Civil Engineers was founded in 1852.

The rapid rise of technology was creating the clear need for a supply of these "captains of industry," and was providing ample material rewards. The teaching of science, however, continued to lag behind in most places. At the universities, despite the great technological transformation already well under way, many science courses were discontinued between 1820 and 1840 for lack of interest. The teaching of science was taken most seriously at the Scottish universities and at the Royal College of Chemistry of London (1845). The practice finally penetrated to Oxford and Cambridge in the late Fifties, but did not find a leading place until a generation later.

It is, of course, true that individual scientists contributed to the Industrial Revolution in various ways. Euler wrote a book on the mathematical theory of gear wheels as early as 1760. James Watt derived many sound hints for improving the efficiency of the steam engine from Joseph Black's lectures on heat. However, such instances were relatively rare. The principal work of technological innovation and development was done by experienced craftsmen and inventors who made brave attempts to produce quantitative data that might be useful to others. With the aid of the few interested scientists, notably Coulomb, Réaumur, Van Musschenbroek, and Gauthey, they invented machines for testing such materials as stone, timber, and metals. The data they obtained were relative only, since applied mechanics did not develop until the next century, but at any rate they had found the proper way of trying to understand and put to use the theoretical background of their trade. And they needed not only instruction for the leaders; they also had to find a source of skilled labour to run their machinery.

Competent workers for the new factories were not easily come by. As late as the early part of the 19th century elementary education was still rare for the masses, and a large proportion of the population was unable to read or write. The lack of training in elementary science at school made it difficult to provide proper technical training in the factory or shop, and the limited availability of skilled labour long slowed the development of the new technology.

The Vanishing Crafts

The 18th century taught engineers that industrialization implied a complete break with the past. Craftsmen had worked at home or in workshops for generations, and the early inventors of the Industrial Revolution still thought in these terms. Larger buildings, which since antiquity had accommodated a number of craftsmen of the same type, and the early monastic establishments, where people could rent the energy of the water wheel for their work, bore some resemblance to modern factories. But the word was not even used in its present sense in the 18th century. A "factory" was a shop, a warehouse, or a depot, and it was not until the end of the century that the term was sometimes applied to the machine-dominated assemblies that were beginning to develop in the modern mode.

James Watt and his generation spoke of "mills," since the first thing that caught their eye was the large water wheel, the prime mover; hence we still hear of cotton mills, flour mills, etc. The first legal use of the word factory was in the Textile Factory Act of 1844. The term was applied to Lombe's silk factory and to early textile mills adopting the steam engine. Thus the word took on its modern meaning as an establishment where prime movers make a variety of machinery work by a system of power transmission.

The mechanization of various manual operations that led from home to mill to factory ended the era of the craftsman. Machinery took over a phase, or even an entire operation, out of the series of acts leading from raw material to end product. The craftsman had been trained in all these operations as an apprentice and thus qualified as a master of his material; it was on his individual technical skill that the quality of the product depended. Now machinery imitated and standardized his manual operations; and quality control of the product depended upon technical tests carried out, usually automatically, all along the line of production machines. In this process the personal capacities of the workmen were of little consequence. The new job classifications—engineer, foreman, skilled labour, unskilled labour, apprentice—no longer implied an upward progression as a man acquired and perfected skills on the job. The machines became more and more complicated; they and the tools they contained worked with a precision the craftsman could never attain. If he were intelligent and properly trained, he could make the machine work efficiently, but this was an impersonal skill. In the great transition between 1750 and 1850 "craft" became "job." Nowadays only a very few crafts are left, and their number is rapidly decreasing under the economic impact of mass production and the technological impact of increasingly sophisticated machinery.

From Steam to Atomic Energy

The Industrial Revolution gained full impact around 1850 when experimental science had put its house in order. During the first half of the century, mathematics and mechanics produced elaborate, well-organized bodies of knowledge, not only able to cope with engineering problems but constantly probing their own basic axioms and already casting doubt on some of Newton's dogma. Optics and acoustics as well as the new theory of magnetism and electricity were being developed. With Lavoisier alchemy had come to an end and modern quantitative chemistry was born; in the hands of Dalton, Dumas, Berzelius, and many others the new science branched into analytical, inorganic, organic, physical, and bio-chemistry. Important compounds, formerly known only as contaminated natural products or hidden in natural mixtures, were isolated, among them coal tar and petroleum. New raw materials for industrial production and synthesis of drugs and medicines, dyes, foodstuffs, fertilizers and pesticides, fibres, and plastics were discovered. But above all, the new thermodynamics provided a sound theoretical background for the design of steam engines, the measurement of their thermal efficiency, the development of refrigeration, and many other practical applications of the theory of heat.

Coal and iron were the symbols of the new machine age, and the steam engine was its prime mover. It made possible railways, and land travel broke out of speed limits set two thousand years earlier by the Roman postal system. Steam was applied to navigation and produced concentrations of power for moving ships that soon exceeded any prime mover used on land. The engines of the "Great Western" (1837) were rated at 750 hp., those of the "Great Britain" (1843), at 1,500 hp. Such large steam engines were slow to be introduced in industry, but the production of cheap steel since the days of Bessemer (1856) and the recognition that only high steam temperatures (and hence high pressures) could improve thermal efficiency gradually induced industry to install larger and more powerful units. By 1880, 400-hp. steam units were by no means exceptional, and by the turn of the century 8,000 hp. were fairly common and a few reached the 10,000–12,000 range. This represented the ultimate development of such engines; a 10,000-hp. unit built for the New York City subway in 1899 was put on the scrap heap in 1902. The old model towered 40 ft. into the air, whereas a new type of engine, the steam turbine, only one-tenth its size and consuming far less coal, had comparable capacity.

The steam turbines, first introduced in 1882 by Carl De Laval, came to be intimately linked with electricity. This development took some time, for the complex processes of generating, transforming, and transporting AC, DC, and rotating current had to be investigated and developed, but by 1906 the larger new electric power plants installed steam turbines. Thirty years later, units of 85,000 kw. at 1,500 revolutions per minute doubled the output of energy from coal, as compared with the output of 1910, and produced forty to fifty times as much energy as Newcomen's steam engines did before the days of James Watt.

A remote cousin of the old Norse mill also became an important factor in producing electricity. In the late 1860s, Bergès, a Grenoble papermaker, realized that water tumbling down from the Alps could be used as a new "fuel," which he called *houille blanche* ("white coal"). The water turbine, improved a century before by Euler and Fourneyron, first drove Bergès' paper machines, but soon was harnessed to dynamos in power plants. By the end of the 19th century electricity was generated by water turbines at the great Niagara Falls in the United States, and the process was spreading across the highlands of the Western world.

The water turbine is still the most efficient prime mover, capable of converting 92–93 percent of the energy of falling water into power. Electricity solved the difficulty of transporting this converted waterpower from remote mountain valleys where it was not needed. New possibilities opened for countries short of fossil fuel and consequently still underdeveloped. Parts of Scandinavia, France, Italy, and Switzerland were rich in this "white coal," and the first decades of the present century saw the beginnings of a tremendous development of hydroelectric power in these areas.

The manufacture of metallurgical coke produced gas as

a by-product and created a flourishing gas industry for illumination. Inventors like Rochas and Lenoir soon tried their hand at a gas engine. Nikolaus Otto, who in 1862 had invented the four-stroke cycle, succeeded in making the first successful gas engine (patented 1877). It was later equipped with electric ignition. The first stationary internal-combustion engine led to a mobile version, the four-cycle engine (1855), which Daimler and Benz adapted independently to construct the first motor cars. The new engine used a new fuel, gasoline, originally a by-product of the refining of crude oil for the production of lubricants and kerosene; by 1900 gasoline was the main product of the young oil industry. The diesel engine, using heavier fuels, was patented in 1893 and soon appeared in heavy road transport and marine engineering since it was thermally 4 to 5 times as efficient as the steam engine. By the early 1920s ships moved by diesel engines sailed the seas, and trucks with diesel engines came into use; large diesel units of 10,000 kw. and over are now used in power plants. The internal-combustion engine, its weight cut by engineering research from 4.5 pounds per horsepower in 1900 to 1.1 pounds in 1950, completely conquered transport by road, sea, and air, and played a major part in mechanizing agriculture. Meanwhile the turbine continues to take on new forms: a gas version was applied to aircraft propulsion by Sir Frank Whittle (1930) and perfected in 1946, ushering in a new era of rocket and jet engines.

The increasing mobility of energy sources—the mass transportation of fuels (pipelines) and electricity (grids) —has now virtually freed industry of the traditional restrictions of geography. Keeping pace with the greatly improved means of communication, this plentiful energy supply has spread the industrial age far beyond the limits of its European origin, and no part of the world is now physically beyond its reach.

As late as 1800 man derived most of the energy he needed for heating, cooking, and manufacturing from farm refuse and wood, a situation that still prevails in many underdeveloped countries just now being reached by the power grids. Against that standard the energy available to the industrial nations has increased twenty to two-hundredfold and more. Technology, together with the conversion of energy from one form into another (always with inherent losses) and the production and transportation of fuels, consumes only about half the total amount. The other half is used to suppy man with the necessities and amenities of life.

The shift in energy sources has had a profound economic, political, and cultural impact on modern society. The steam engine placed a great emphasis on coal and iron, and thus determined the rate of industrialization of various countries. For example, after an excellent start in imitating and sometimes outstripping early British industry, and contributing a full share of important technological inventions, France fell behind for lack of coal; as late as 1846 60 percent of her pig iron was smelted in small charcoal furnaces. German conquest of the iron ore deposits of eastern Lorraine in 1871 was another blow. France did not catch up with the trend of concentrating men and machinery in efficient mass-production factories until hydroelectric power and its mobile electric energy reached the suburbs of Paris and other important cities. The prevailing tendency during this great era of expansion was to combine more and more phases of industry in large comprehensive complexes handling all operations from raw material to final product. Nations that had the means to do this moved out in front.

While the technologists were perfecting the production and transmission of energy from what are now the conventional sources, the scientists were opening still another frontier. During the 1930s techniques were developed for the use of energy contained in the atom, and engineers have now solved the problem of turning this idea to practical use—as well as into great new engines of military destruction. On October 17, 1956, the first nuclear power station opened at Calder Hall, Cumberland, to be followed by an American plant at Shippingport, Pennsylvania, on December 2, 1957. The conversion of the energy of the atom into electric power is still not economically competitive for most applications, and the contribution to the world's energy supply from this source is still relatively small. There are, however, atomic "prime movers" in service on ships, even as the first big steam engines found their place on the seas. The process is available and there can be little doubt that in time it will see wide use.

Sources of Knowledge

The development of new energy sources, and their application to expanding industry have required a new, close cooperation between science and technology. Basic scientific research, *i.e.*, investigation of the physical and chemical properties of various substances and of the structure of matter, has of course long been a part of the university curriculum. Now, however, it is often indirectly joined with industrial research, sometimes called applied research. Here general information on required physical and chemical properties is treated as "engineering science." Industrial research differs from fundamental or basic research in that the knowledge needed for this kind of development is made up of layers, like those of an onion in the characterization given by R. J. Seeger:

> A question at any one level is dependent immediately upon information contained in the layer directly beneath it; the answer there, in turn, can be applied at a layer just above. Hence basic or applied is largely a matter of viewpoint. The top layers represent applied research, the bottom layers basic research. Social progress has proved critically sensitive to the depth of the probing; we descend from technological needs to more scientific questions and at each step basic and applied research is needed.

A new type of research teamwork has developed, distinctively different from that traditional in the university laboratory. Industrial research teams commonly combine theorists, experimentalists, and plant engineers. The results reached in the laboratory are first translated into industrial language. Then they were applied in pilot plants, where secondary features of new processes such as the effect of apparatus design can be observed under controlled conditions. Cost factors are projected and applied against market research and other data. Generally speaking, only the larger industries can afford such research; in the United States, now the leader in the field, $5,370,000,000 was spent for research purposes in 1953, with 44 percent contributed by private industry itself, 52 percent by the government (largely by the Department of Defense), and the remaining 4 percent by universities and foundations. Out of this total, 72 percent was spent in industrial research laboratories, 18 percent in government laboratories, 1 percent in miscellaneous agencies, and 9 percent in university laboratories. The total amount spent on research continues to rise and although the breakdown varies, the percentages given are not changing significantly. It is now normal for industrial firms to spend 3 to 4 percent of their budget on research; in some fields, such as pharmaceuticals and electronics, the figure goes up to 8 percent. Generally speaking, the state assists the smaller industries which cannot afford to spend large sums by supporting the research in state or subsidized private laboratories and disseminating the results.

Stimulated by the post-World War II wave of public and private research, engineering has broken down into specialties wholly unknown in the past. The parent profession, civil engineering, is now divided among specialists dealing with the specifics of highway and railroad construction, hydraulics, water supply and sewage treatment, and irrigation. The mechanical, metallurgical, electrical, structural, chemical, mining, and aeronautical engineers of two generations ago are supplemented by experts in toolmaking, applied thermodynamics, radio, telephone and television, power and automation, welding and illumination, safety and fire protection. All these are being trained at universities or technical institutes, sometimes in conjunction with the "pure" scientists.

The industrial process itself has undergone radical changes. A century ago an industry comprised the series of operations individual craftsman had formerly executed, translated into mechanical operations under the supervision of a works engineer, who had to know the ins and outs of the entire line of operations in order to run his plant.

In 1760, at the very beginning of the Industrial Revolution, Jean Perronet had understood that quantitative measures could be devised to integrate men, materials, and equipment in such a way that a higher productivity per man-hour could be attained. Eli Whitney and Simeon North tried their hand at this new science in the 1790s, and both Robert Owen (1813) and Charles Babbage (1820) studied the manufacture of pins in order to establish a rational sequence of manufacture by machinery. In 1881, at the Midvale Steel Company of Philadelphia, Frederick Taylor began his "time study," which he presented in his classic work of 1903. This book, together with Frank B. and Lillian M. Gilbreth's *Motion Study* (1911), launched a new phase of "industrial" engineering in Great Britain and the United States between 1910 and 1930 which produced techniques that have become an essential part of the industrial process everywhere.

The new techniques are typified in the chemical industry, where the old sequences were transformed into *unit operations* and processes as early as the 1890s. The relatively few basic operations, either physical (heating, drying, crushing, shredding, mixing, filtering, settling, distilling) or chemical (oxidation, reduction, chlorination, polymerization, catalytic treatment), were studied and elaborated by experts who then applied the latest results of scientific research in these fields. The large modern factories built thereafter gradually became conglomerations of such apparatus as was needed for the entire operation that transformed raw materials into finished products, all fully controlled by new automatic registering instruments. The combination of the old manufacturing processes into such units made the factories more adaptable to the introduction of new techniques and the production of new end products. This development also gave rise to the specialization that combined two technical disciplines, commemorated by the founding of the American Institute of Chemical Engineers in 1908.

Mass production of consumer goods was made possible by this kind of industrial engineering. Large-scale manufacture of standard commodities demands long production runs and continuous plant operation. Specialized production and material-handling equipment, well-planned sequence of handling, and division of labour into the performance of short and simple operations under proper controls are required for a stable economic basis. This pattern is fundamental for the assembly-line operations, which became possible with the development of standardized interchangeable parts. Now even the last strongholds of the craftsmen, in the fabrication of ships, bridges, and skyscrapers, have been reduced to the routine assembly of standard parts machine-made in mass production factories.

Spread of Standardization

The possibility of control and efficiency to be gained by reducing variations in their product has always attracted technologists; it was recognized in the standardized orifices used by the Imperial Roman Water Board. In the 16th century the artillery schools and arsenals of Spain, Austria, and other countries began to lay down detailed specifications for artillery and firearms, thus making possible interchangeable cannon balls and bullets. Prince Maurice of Orange took a notable part in the standardization of smaller firearms, and the uniforms, drill, and tactics of the armies of those days began to reflect the trend. Along the long route to Java the Dutch East India Company built stations where ships could stop to victual and pick up standard parts (*e.g.,* blocks, ropes, and sails) that had to be replaced. In the second Anglo-Dutch War (1665-67) the Dutch fleet was reinforced with a number of standard warships built under emergency conditions, the forerunners of the Liberty ships of World War II.

As mechanized production of machine parts progressed and machine tools were developed, the new precision provided the basis for standardizing such items as bolts, screws, and nuts, which became interchangeable once they were no longer handmade; later, iron and steel bars and sheet iron also were produced in standard sizes. The engineer no longer had to manufacture for himself all the parts of each new engine or piece of machinery as had Boulton and Watt; he could assemble what he needed from the common supply.

The use of interchangeable parts was well established in Europe and America in the 19th century. They made possible the planting and harvesting machinery that transformed agriculture and ushered in an era of food surpluses. They were fundamental in the rise of mass production, and modern technology as a whole is now based on standardization of products, materials, methods, and equipment. We have codified engineering and safety standards for technical work, the properties of the materials used, fits and tolerances, and the terminology in common use. Specifications, inspection, and test methods aimed at ever greater precision are under constant review in the light of a flood of new data. Worldwide interchange between standardizing bodies is, of course, essential and it has survived two world wars.

The assembly line was a perhaps inevitable outgrowth of the manufacture of interchangeable parts. It now became possible to group workers along a moving belt in a factory, so that a number of simple and specialized operations could be performed on each unit as it moved past each worker in turn. Eli Whitney tried to adapt the idea to his musket factory as far back as 1798, and the concept was revived in other industries over the years. But lasting success did not come until the assembly line was applied to the manufacture of motor cars; in 1912-13 Henry Ford reorganzed his Highland Park factory to accommodate the new method that was to become a symbol of the automobile industry.

The logical next step in this development was automation. The history of technology is the story of the gradual mechanization of manual labour. On the assembly line it was possible to develop techniques to take over not only physical but also mental tasks. Gradually human attendance was required only to check on whether the machines performed their predetermined assignments properly. The next step was automatic machines performing complex tasks under automatic control. In the post-World War II years control systems were refined to the point where whole operations could be set in motion, maintained, and safeguarded against error without human intervention after the starting button was pushed.

This kind of automation has been a traditional goal of the technologist. The Jacquard loom (1801) represents the combined efforts of three generations of inventors who struggled with the problem of constructing a machine that would respond to a controlled, preset pattern while retaining the possibilities of making different weaves as on a hand-operated loom. This was achieved by means of perforated cards, arranged in long bands or books passing through the loom. The perforations of these cards formed the "code" on which the loom acted and produced such weaves as the signals commanded it to make—the principle embodied in the most sophisticated of modern control machinery.

Control mechanisms may be mechanical, hydraulic, pneumatic, or electronic; sometimes combinations are used. A thermostat maintains a fixed output of heat independent of input variations; it exercises what engineers call "feedback" control in that the deviation of the system is used as a restoring force. More modern control systems are called *servomechanisms* (servos). They are able to adjust output automatically to input and consist of a sensing (error-determining) element, an amplifier, and a servomotor. Such systems have made possible unmanned space ships and satellities; they also are of great importance in automated factories where the timing of the cycle of processes is governed by electric signals. These servomechanisms are the product of the proliferating new electronics industry and its diodes, transistors, pulse shapers, and amplifiers, but the theoretical background of these decision-making control mechanisms was formed by the new science of cybernetics.

The word *cybernetics* was coined by André Ampère in 1834 to denote the "science of control." It was used by Norbert Wiener to indicate "the study of control and communication in the animal and the machine," which he was able to develop, aided by two branches of applied mathematics: information theory and dynamic programming. The first of these, started by Szilard and Nyquist in the early 1920s, dealt with the characteristics, properties, and functions of any signal system designed to transmit information. Thus it dealt with filtering and predicting, decision-making and estimating, coding and decoding, and it was applied with success to the study of languages. The second dealt with the problems of multistage decision processes. Cybernetics was first used to design mechanisms for military guidance and fire-control systems during World War II. Later it became the standard tool for designers of control equipment for automatic machinery complexes. The processing of information found its first industrial application in the chemical industry and in the telephone system, and thus was born the computer, which seems to be ushering in a new technological age.

Advent of the Computer

The automatic data processor, popularly miscalled an electronic brain, is a direct descendant of that oldest of computing machines, the abacus, widely used in antiquity and still in use in many parts of Asia. In the course of the centuries many attempts were made to mechanize such machines; Pascal constructed the first adding machine with countergears (1642); Leibniz (1694) improved it so that multiplication and addition became possible on the same machine; and this finally gave rise to the modern desk calculator. Charles Babbage worked on a rudimentary digital computer in the 1830s, but the first automatic general-purpose device did not appear until 1944. It was titled the IBM Harvard Automatic Sequence Controlled Calculator, and two years later the first electronic computer, the ENIAC, was built.

The computer performs a sequence of mathematical or logical operations in response to information data coded into numbers, words, or other symbols. The machine is an assembly of six units. The input unit takes data or instructions translated into suitable machine language (punched cards or polarized spots on magnetic tape). The storage unit registers this information in machine language. The arithmetic unit performs calculations—additions, subtractions, multiplications, and divisions—and returns the result to the storage unit. The bus or trunk transfers the information by wire from one part of the computer to the other in the form of electric pulses. The control unit takes successive instructions from the storage unit and issues commands to switches in the machine, controlling the connections of the bus and registers. The output unit takes the computer answers and translates the machine language back into printed characters or the like. The capacity of the computer, a rigidly controlled electronic instrument, is, of course, determined by the information fed into it.

Computers are in increasing use in science, business, medicine, manufacturing, communications, military and government operations, and education—indeed, it is difficult to imagine any field except that of the most personal services where they cannot be adapted in some fashion. Computers provide selective access to libraries and large files of documents, and they allow the numerical processing of data at an incredible speed. They handle information far beyond the limits of human memory and may perform at high speed calculations that a man would need a lifetime to do. The principal assets are speed of handling data, accuracy, and reliability.

The simplest of the machines can be programmed to substitute for the skilled labour once employed in surveying and controlling the phases of an industrial process. They can perform as intelligence amplifiers for a reliable performance of complex routines or programs. By feedback automatic control, utilizing interaction of signals from sensing devices together with previously acquired information stored in the memory units, they can be entrusted with the simpler forms of decision-making. And, of course, they are tireless and free of the emotional distractions that account for the errors made by the mere humans they have replaced at many critical points in the technological order.

The Automatic Technology

The role of labour in the computer-dominated automatic technology already has been drastically altered. It cannot yet be said, however, that this latest phase of the Industrial Revolution has proceeded evenly in accord with its technological imperative. In some fields, such as structural engineering, automation has hardly started, even though housing shortages in many countries would seem to prompt its adaptation. Farming has been highly mechanized in the United States, with a great displacement of agricultural labour, and comparable mechanization is proceeding rapidly elsewhere. But other activities, such as fishing, seem hardly touched by the new technology.

The rate of change is clearly altered by social and economic conditions that have nothing directly to do with the limitations or possibilities of the new technology. This, of course, has always been the case, and it is the residue of the uneven past development of the technological order that presents us with the sharpest contrasts in the contemporary world. Our automated Western economy now provides us with one candle hour of light produced by an electric bulb at one-sixtieth of the cost of a century ago. This is the product of the efficient use of energy under a system that has not yet reached most of the world. African smiths, still using methods that have changed little since the early Iron Age, would require 40,000 man-hours to produce one ton of the metal that is smelted in Pittsburgh in two hours.

Most Westerners would accept these comparisons as indications that there have been far more gainers than losers in the course of the Industrial Revolution, if human progress in fact can be measured in material terms. It is not surprising then, that by the turn of the present century large numbers of people had been converted to technology as a sort of materialistic faith. The growing cooperation of science and technology was accompanied by a rising standard of living that seemed to confirm the principles enunciated in the days of the Great Exhibition of 1851 by a small circle under the leadership of Prince Albert. Their prophet was Francis Bacon, who had said in *The New Atlantis*, "We have many reasons to believe that Nature still carries many Secrets of Great Profit, which are hardly related to those already known, which are still unperceived and beyond the Scope of our Imagination." Now these wonders of material progress were at hand, and why should one not accept also Bacon's dictum: "Therefore Truth and Profit are one here and the Works themselves are of greater value than Assurances of the Truthfulness [of Theories] because they add to the Pleasures of Life?" It seemed that the final control of man's environment would put an end to poverty and sickness, and that this great human goal was now within reach. For in science, too, popular prophets such as Haeckel had declared that the last secrets of Nature would be unraveled within his lifetime, and that man would thereby become master of his fate.

In academic and intellectual circles this faith in material progress was not always widely shared; on the contrary, scholars and moralists challenged the value of many of the technological achievements and feared that the mechanization of life would destroy the world of the spirit within a few generations. Would not this material progress run away with mankind and lead it to perdition? Some of these pessimists raked up the old arguments Bacon's opponents had used against his "experimental science." They are still heard today among the generations of the first half of this century, which passed through two world wars and took part in the explosive development of technology that exceeds in quality and quantity all that has gone before.

PART TWO

MACHINE AND MILIEU

LIKE THE TREE in the Garden of Eden, technology has brought boons and curses; it is, after all, the product of man's intellect and his hands. The catalog of changes it has produced in the quality of our daily lives covers most of the essentials. The enduring concerns of prehistoric man in procuring light, heat, and food, out of which the great technological quest was born, have been reduced to automatic routine for millions in the Western world.

A hundred years ago heating was still a grave problem, even for the rich. The wealthy 17-century scientist Christiaan Huygens calculated each year how many trees he would have to plant in his park if he was to have sufficient firewood to keep his country seat warm in wintertime. The stoves and open-hearth fires of the 18th century were a matter of concern and considerable attention for so accomplished a man of parts as Benjamin Franklin. We were near the end of the 19th century before the larger towns in the most advanced countries had water and fuel supplies readily available for the central heating and limitless hot water moderns take for granted.

During that same century the Western world still reckoned its food supplies in terms of the vagaries of seasons and years. In many regions much of the livestock had to he slaughtered in autumn and the meat preserved by smoking, salting, or bottling, because of the lack of fodder to tide the cattle over the winter. In the absence of modern means of preservation and rapid transportation the great majority of people faced the prospect of a limited and unbalanced diet during the cold months when vegetables and fruits disappeared from their tables. In a little more than fifty years the technologists have employed machinery and chemicals to work an agricultural miracle.

Pioneers such as Théodore de Saussure and Justus von Liebig led the way to the production of fertilizers, the introduction of nitrates from Chile and Peru, and the extraction of phosphates from blast furnace slags. By 1900 nitrogen from the air could be fixed to compete with the natural nitrates; twenty years later fumigants were synthesized and pesticides came into wide use to protect crops against destruction by insects and plant disease. New rotation and fertilizing cycles made possible entirely new crops to meet the increasing demand that followed lower prices and expanding markets, and the introduction of machinery began to turn the farms into "food factories."

Supplies from overseas to maintain the sharply rising populations of the Western world became possible as machines were harnessed for long-distance transport of foodstuffs. The development of the theory of heat led to mechanical refrigeration and by 1876 ships with vast coolers were in service to bring Europeans meat from as far away as South America and Australia. Deep-freezing techniques, developed about 1911, were soon applied to a great variety of raw foodstuffs, and by 1925 they were adapted to precooked foods to liberate housewives from onerous and time-consuming chores.

The technologists changed the traditional forms of foodstuffs. Von Liebig found a method of preparing a meat extract which could easily be transported in liquid or evaporated form. The manufacture of such extracts started in Uruguay in 1865 and transformed the role of stockbreeding in many remote regions. Meat that had commonly been left to rot on the prairies when cattle were slaughtered for their hides now became the most valuable article produced on the ranches, and supplies for the leather manufacturers fell into the role of by-product. Evaporation techniques were applied to milk by Borden in the same period.

François Appert adapted the techniques long used by housewives to "bottle" foodstuffs to large-scale commercial use, and by 1830 canned meat, fish, and vegetables came into use, initially to meet the special needs of the armed forces and expeditionary parties. The discoveries of Pasteur and his generation put the preservation of food on a solid scientific basis. The technologists pyramided these theories into the giant industry that has developed to process, package, transport, and merchandise the once simple products of farm and field. The progress from test tube to flip-top beer can has transformed the living standards of the West.

This stabilization of food supplies, however, has been limited to only a small part of the world. Vast areas are still overpopulated in relation to their ability to produce sufficient foodstuffs, and hundreds of millions are living on the edge of starvation. It is probable that the technologists can put together the physical means to meet this great challenge of the 20th century. Improved farming techniques, supported by improved water supplies, and linked to modern processing and distribution systems undoubtedly could provide at least subsistence standards for the world's population—which may itself be limited in time by the birth control techniques developed by the modern technologists.

The primary problems here are social, political, and economic. We are now beginning to take note of the cultural impact on underdeveloped countries of the introduction of modern farming techniques, and we are finding difficulties far beyond the elementary matter of teaching the natives to handle the new machinery. Changing the type of agriculture literally changes the way of life, for agriculture is deeply rooted in the material civilization of these countries and rapid, basic change can offset its undoubted benefits with a profound disruption of the social fabric.

The reason for this is obvious when one considers the dramatic result of the mechanization of agriculture in the advanced countries—the wholesale displacement of millions of farm workers in a single generation. Farmers have always sought to reduce the amount of labour that goes into agricultural production, a matter of economics as well as comfort. The earliest reapers of Roman Gaul were designed in a period when the supply of slaves was beginning to drop. So, centuries later, development of the mechanical harvester and the cotton-picking machine gained impetus from the rising cost of free farm labour. The ingenious farm machines were limited in their application, however, so long as they required both man and horse to provide energy. The revolution began with the adaptation of the internal-combustion engine to the farm tractor around 1915. By the 1930s the combine had appeared, a single machine that moved across the fields as it reaped and threshed wheat, bound the straw, and packed the grain in sacks, literally turning the farm into a factory. Parallel developments have taken place for virtually all food and fibre.

Two examples illustrate this rapid invasion of the farm by technology. In England and Wales supplies of power to farms rose from 1,000,000 hp. in 1908 to double that figure in 1939 and to 5,500,000 hp. in 1948; in the same years, horses contributed 87, 24, and 7 percent of the power needed. Manpower decreased to one-fourth during these forty years.

In the United States 71.8 percent of the available labour force worked on the land in 1820; by 1950 this figure had fallen to 11.6 percent. If the methods and crops of 1820 had been reintroduced, some 46 million hands would have been required to maintain the production level, which would have meant that 39,800,000 men would have had to be withdrawn from other occupations to help man the farms.

Not only was population redistributed as a consequence of the agricultural revolution but man's total environment was affected. Along with the mechanized technology, scientific research produced controlled genetic changes in livestock, hybrid seeds, new chemical fertilizers, and chemical pesticides (DDT is the most famous) for eliminating noxious insects and pests. The excessive use of these new substances in many areas has produced man-made changes in environment which have altered ecology in a fashion that caused Rachel Carson to warn of impending disaster in her notable book, *Silent Spring.*

By midcentury the agricultural technologists had even gone to sea, turning their attention to new food resources hardly tapped over the centuries. Fishing is as old as man, but from a technological point of view development of the fishing industry has just begun. Science has already provided a theoretical basis for new industries that may use a variety of forms of life from the sea for world food supplies. The exploration of the deeper layers of the oceans, the study of plankton and similar simpler forms of oceanic organic life, have been given new impetus by the need for additional materials to feed the rapidly growing world population.

The Communications Revolution

The new forms of communication that have speeded up the transport of information, goods, and human beings at a still accelerating rate also are less than a century old. In the time of Napoleon the rate of movement for land traffic was no greater than it had been in the heyday of the Roman Empire. It was only when steam power produced the first railways in Great Britain that man could exceed the speed of a fast horse. In the 1800s McAdam was informed by members of Parliament that the days of new highway construction were past; it was assumed that the obvious advantages of rail transport would quickly eliminate road traffic. Something like this did happen in the Age of Steam, but by the turn of the century the internal-combustion engine had been applied to road vehicles. The railways, many of them electrified to attain greater economy and efficiency, have lost much of their passenger traffic to road and air transport in the United States and face a similar fate in other countries. Steamships, too, the technical marvels that replaced the graceful sailing vessels on the high seas, are rapidly being reduced to plodding haulers of freight by their high-flying competition. It is expected that some of the developing countries will leap directly from stone-age transport to primary reliance on air transport and never develop anything approximating the rail, road, and waterway systems that characterized the older industrial nations.

This latest major entry in the field of transport did not arrive effectively until the late 1920s. As the child of the new age the aircraft industry has been a showcase of new technologies. The introduction of aluminum and its alloys met the requirement of great strength with low weight. The need for light but ever more powerful engines led to turboprop and jet-power plants. The demands of increasing speed resulted in new instruments for better and safer navigation, culminating in the automatic pilot and other airborne adaptations of the computer. The curve is still upward in the speed and size of aircraft, as they move into dominant position in all forms of transport except the purely local.

Train and boat, motor car and airplane, not only have speeded up transportation—they have added important new dimensions to trade and commerce. They have made it possible to reorganize and greatly expand the distribution of industrial products and open up new markets almost without regard to previous geographical limitations. The effect of the rapid development in communications on power politics was made evident by two great wars that properly included "world" in their titles.

Equally spectacular has been the revolution in human communication, largely based on various applications of electricity. In sequence, the engineers produced the telegraph, telephone, radio, and television, and found ways to put those devices into almost universal service in the West. Photography was combined with recorded sound to produce a new medium of mass entertainment. In a single generation men were exposed to the experiences of others in a way not even the most fortunate of their ancestors had known.

Communication with other human beings changes the personal environment in profound ways. In the beginning, communication was limited to those a man could see and hear. Then he produced artifacts which served as a record and a precept for others and which thus became a store of knowledge. Man learned to project speech by writing and to disseminate writing by printing, but the most fully effective way of communicating with other human beings has remained personal. Travel in the early days was truly educational; it was the means by which a favoured few established contact with an entirely different world of ideas and practices. Its essence was the reciprocity that is often lost in the dehumanization and speeding up of the new forms of communication.

Whether it serves to limit or enhance the inherent possibilities or the critical faculty in man, there can be no doubt of the profound effect of the new communication net that envelops us all. John Diebold in *Beyond Automation* has written: "It would be difficult to overstate the magnitude of change that will take place in the lives of all of us, in human history, as a result of the information revolution that has so unobtrusively taken place in our day. Information, its communication and use, is the web of so-

them; new chemicals, such as household detergents, cannot be eliminated from industrial and effluent water by conventional chemical and bacteriological treatment methods. In many cases, this becomes an international issue; for example, industrial pollution of the Rhine, whose waters serve several countries, can only be prevented by international cooperation involving the establishment of common standards and effective laws to enforce them. Although much polluted or otherwise wasted water can be recovered and added to the water supply if such political obstacles can be overcome, there is already an urgent need for entirely new sources. The technologists have lately turned to the sea, and the first atomic desalinization plants were in service by 1965.

Sanitary and biological engineering is also faced with increasing problems of air pollution. This again is a problem that has faced city authorities through the ages, wherever the crafts flourished. In antiquity, leather workers and dyers were usually banished to quarters on the outskirts of town because of the offense given by the urine and other smelly chemicals used in their workshops. By 1600 soot was added to odour as more and more "sea coale" was shipped down from Newcastle upon Tyne for use in the City of London. Queen Elizabeth refused to come into the city for an entire year because of the polluted air, and in 1661 John Evelyn dedicated his *Fumifugium* to King Charles II, proposing to banish industries to the southern bank of the Thames in order to combat the "smoake of London," which affected men, trees, and houses alike.

During the last century the evil has been aggravated by the expanding use of coal and oil by industry and for heating homes and public buildings. Under special geographical and climatological conditions ("inversion") combustion gases, along with the fumes from chemical and other industries, tend to accumulate in the atmosphere above major cities. The old City of London has now been joined by the new City of Los Angeles in the list of those most notorious for a kind of "smog" that is not only unpleasant but a threat to public health. The exhaust gases of gasoline and diesel engines are now recognized as major contributors to smog formation, and, since the number of motor cars continues to increase, the attack must involve millions of individual citizens instead of a relatively few industrial sources. Here the technologists have clearly gotten ahead of the researchers; we not only have not been able to turn back the rate of air pollution except in isolated cases, but we know little about the diseases caused by contaminated air or about the aggravation of latent diseases among city dwellers.

Collection and disposal of industrial refuse and garbage is rapidly taking a top place on the agenda of urban problems. Municipal scavenging only began about a century ago; in the 18th century cries of "gardeelu" still warned pedestrians that garbage was being flung from upper windows into the open gutter in the middle of the street. The modern refuse problem is not simply that the quantity is increasing disproportionately to the number of citizens but that its nature has become more and more varied. The sewage sludge and dustbins of two generations ago contained practically nothing but kitchen offal and cinders from the stoves. This material could readily be transformed into commercial fertilizer by composting, or be incinerated and used for road building. The introduction of new materials into the household, particularly insoluble chemical detergents and commercial nonreturn containers of plastic, glass, and metal now require that the garbage be sifted, and this added complication and cost has made the conversion of much refuse unprofitable. We now have well-organized, motorized collection and transportation systems for our sewage and garbage, but no good way to dispose of what they collect. A White House conference in 1966 devoted much attention to the comparable problem of disposing of the abandoned automobiles which dot the American landscape in increasing numbers because previous scrapping methods have become uneconomic even as annual motor car production continued to set new records. And still more new difficulties in the disposal of industrial refuse lie ahead as radioactive substances become more abundant with the growth of atomic power plants and industries and laboratories using radioactive substances.

If the other major problems of the modern city cannot be traced so directly to technological change, some connection is almost always evident. It can even be argued that it was technology which required and made possible the massing of so many people in small areas, and this, of course, is the heart of the issue. Past generations identified the growth of their cities with progress and failed to foresee the physical and human deterioration that would blight them with slums; they failed to make provision for the open spaces that would meet the needs of recreation and modern working and living patterns. Now, with hindsight, the planning of urban development has become universal, but it cannot be said to be wholly successful anywhere. The past often ties the hands of planners, who are locked into existing patterns by previous technical installations such as sewers, water mains, and lines of communication.

The Future Energy Supply

In earlier phases of technological development the problems of maintaining or increasing the supply of energy per capita could be solved locally and almost automatically. With the mechanization of the crafts, however, and the rise of factory technology, the demand for energy supplies increased rapidly. Energy now accounts for 10-25 percent of the cost of production in heavy industry and transport. Only in the textile industry and in the handling and preservation of foodstuffs does this percentage fall below 5 percent. The amount of energy consumed by the industrial nations in 1860 was the equivalent of 135 million tons of coal; except during the economic crisis of the 1930s and during the two world wars, the rate of consumption of energy has increased by about 4 percent a year ever since, doubling in sixteen years. The current rate of increase is closer to 5 percent a year.

This was made possible by the availability of large supplies of two fuels: coal and oil. Hydraulic energy is basic in only a few mountainous countries, and large dams are now likely to be built primarily to obtain water for irrigation. Until 1920, coal was the most important fossil fuel, but the use of oil and natural gas has increased until their production has now slightly outstripped that of coal.

If the rise in the consumption of energy is put at the conservative figure of 4 percent a year, by A.D. 2000 we shall need the equivalent in coal, that is four to five times the amount we now consume. Scientists usually express the total amount of energy consumed over a long period of years in a unit called Q, which is equivalent to 10^{18} BTU (26 billion tons of oil or 37 billion tons of coal). It is estimated that from prehistoric times to 1850, mankind consumed an amount of energy equivalent to 6–9 Q; from 1850 to 1960, some 5 Q; and we shall presumably need some 100 Q during the next century.

There is no doubt that there is a limit to the amount of fossil fuels available. The geology of the world's coal fields is well known; most are found in the northern hemisphere, along a line ranging from the United States through Europe and the U.S.S.R. to China. Lesser resources are located in South America, South Africa, and Australia. So far as oil and gas are concerned, estimates are more problematic. Major new discoveries are still possible, as demonstrated by the recent location of natural gas beneath the North Sea. Theoretically, oil might also be produced from vast deposits of oil shales and tar sands in Canada, Colorado, Brasilia, and other places, but extraction methods are still at the experimental stage. The estimates of so-called proven reserves generally agree that the world's supplies of coal and lignite, and of oil and gas, do not differ significantly, and their total amounts to something like 100-200 Q. This means that energy supplies from fossil fuels could be exhausted within one or two centuries.

These reserves of fossil fuels might be effectively expanded through more efficient means of converting heat into energy, and the technologists continue their study of thermodynamics. But a much more radical solution to the problem of energy sources is already in sight in the release of the powers of the atom. The new trail, opened up in 1896 when Becquerel discovered the radioactivity of uranium salts, and proved out in dreadful practice by the atomic bomb of World War II, has now produced well over a hundred nuclear reactors in peaceful service all over the world. These are still primarily used for research purposes, but the price of the electricity they produce is approaching that of current provided by conventional fuel-fired plants, and they are expected to be able to compete with older power plants within the next decade.

The earth's reserves of uranium are estimated to be between 25 and 30 million tons, theoretically the source of 1500–2500 Q of energy, or enough to meet the world's demands of energy for some two thousand years. But energy also can be obtained by the fusion of two nuclei. The nuclear fusion of deuterium (heavy water) yields far larger quantities of energy than does a fission reaction, but no means are as yet available to handle the resulting gases produced at hundreds of millions of degrees and in such extreme conditions that they have so far defied our technical ingenuity. Should fusion reactors become feasible, the oceans might provide sufficient deuterium to produce 10^{10} Q. As these figures approach the astronomical they can best be understood by homely analogy. Imagine a city of 500,000 inhabitants using electricity from a 250-megawatt power station of the conventional type. Ten kilograms of coal would run this power station for one third of a second, while the fission energy of 10 kg. of hydrogen under present techniques would suffice for three months. Should we acquire the means for freeing all the energy contained in 10 kg. of matter, we would have fuel enough for fifty years of operation.

The Energy Gap

Any estimate of the future demand for energy must, of course, include a number of variables. In the first place there are the figures on the rapidly growing population of the world. This explosive increase of the population might be slowed down by the limited amount of food available in underdeveloped countries, or by war or disease or other causes, and this would undoubtedly affect the rate of growth of energy consumption.

Energy consumption at present follows a pattern of distribution under which 33 percent of the world population consumes 82 percent of the available supply. High energy consumption per capita, one of the measures of a high standard of living, is mainly found in the Western world. In the U.S. about 10 tons of coal a year, or their equivalent in other forms of energy, are consumed per capita, as against 7 in the United Kingdom, 1 in Italy, 10 cwt. in India, and 9 cwt. in Egypt. In most countries, including the U.S., the consumption of energy per capita is still rising, but an African uses only 4 percent, a South American 7½ percent, and an average inhabitant of Asia only 2½ percent of the amount available to the average American.

These differences are due to the mechanization of Western life. The American now uses some 2,500 times as much energy as he did two centuries ago, which means that, in terms of the common energy source of antiquity, he has some sixty slaves at his disposal. A country like Denmark, with a population of just over 4½ million, produces more energy than India with more than 100 times as many inhabitants.

This distribution pattern, and the economic and transport systems it reflects, complicates the problem of raising the living standards of the underdeveloped countries. If we wanted to bring the consumption of energy in India up to that of the Western nations, we should have to transport there the equivalent of one billion tons of coal a year, which is now obviously impossible. Until and unless the scientists and technologists make a great breakthrough, this energy gap is likely to hamper any nonindustrialized country that wishes to follow the lead of the West.

Even within the Western world the problem of fuels is complicated. Coal is relatively cheap in the U.S. in comparison with a price at the pithead in Europe which is about three times as high. The price of oil varies from $2.50 per ton in some fields in the Middle East to ten times that amount for some American crudes, apart from local taxes, the profits retained by the producers, and the cost of transport. Natural gas, which is much cheaper at the source than either coal or oil, has a limiting economic factor in the cost of its transmission by pipeline.

With the advent of nuclear energy, coal and oil may find their prime use as natural resources of chemical and pharmaceutical compounds. As an oil technologist used to say, "Any fool can burn oil," but the application of a little concentrated intelligence has already produced the flourishing new petrochemical industry.

Waste and Conservation

In striking ways technologists have often supplemented limited national resources by finding ways to substitute readily available materials for those in short supply. This ingenuity, however, all too often is brought into play only after man has recklessly squandered the bounty provided by Nature. Tin ores, for instance, from which a metal still essential for modern machinery is extracted, are now found only in a few places, mainly in Malaya, Indonesia, Bolivia, and the Congo. Earlier sources of tin were quite limited, and local supplies were rapidly exhausted in the Western nations. The search for new and richer sources of tin by prospectors and smiths goes back to antiquity and was certainly one of the prime agencies in the spread of technology. Yet, even though we must now go to remote places to get it, a large proportion of the tin in these ores is still lost through careless and wasteful handling. The vast quantity used to coat sheet iron, containers, and canisters lands on the scrap heap or in the garbage can, and is then spread out in so many places it is irrecoverable. This is the prodigal way of the modern "waste makers," as Vance Packard called them.

On the positive side, technologists continue to devise new processes for working low-grade ores ignored until richer grades become rare or are exhausted. Sometimes needed materials can be obtained as a by-product of other industries; and contaminants are often found to have valuable properties. By these means technologists have often ridden to the rescue when private groups, or even nations, have attempted to exploit an apparent monopoly on a needed natural product. It now seems likely that gross attempts to corner the market for industrial raw materials can always be thwarted by the production of substitutes. Nevertheless, there is increasing interest in national and international conservation policies in instances where critical shortages can be foreseen.

In the years 1930-35, oil producers in the United States, and later in Rumania and other countries, combined to slow down total production from exhaustible fields, giving each producer his share and thus removing the incentive for each to take out all he could before the common pool ran dry. In the United States the Connally Act of 1935 gave the sanction of law to those "proration" policies. The technologists can provide the data on world resources necessary for comparable conservation on an international scale—but, of course, there will remain major political problems of how to carry out and enforce such agreements.

Here the technologists, who have to bear their share of guilt for many modern depredations, may take credit for creating conditions that require the nations to work in concert. Measures to prevent the exhaustion of natural resources, to counter the economic consequences of regional overproduction, and to clear the way for the application of advanced technology will have to accompany the effort to spread the high Western standard of living. Tentative though the beginning has been, new international compacts and new international institutions such as the special agencies of the United Nations may be the beginning of a new political order that will follow technology across national boundaries.

Outdoing Nature

Man's effort to exploit natural resources and find new sources of raw materials traditionally has stimulated his technological ingenuity. Thus, some of the rare metals discovered during the 18th and 19th centuries have become valuable constituents of special steels, and what was first a curiosity in the laboratory is now a commonplace of large-scale manufacture. Small pieces of aluminum the size of a button were shown to Napoleon III as a triumph of research without any known use. Today's aircraft and space vehicles are made possible by the rapid growth of a new industry based on light alloys, in which aluminum and its sister elements are in the forefront of a whole range of "new" metals.

The age of synthetic materials began a century ago with the production of synthetic dyes from coal-tar products. Those new dyes soon ousted natural products, such as madder and indigo. Coal and oil since have yielded a whole range of synthetic materials for a wide variety of uses, and the changes in production have also had profound side effects. The shift from stearine to paraffin wax for the manufacture of candles made second-grade fats and oils available for the production of margarine and other products suitable for human consumption. Other edible and otherwise usable fats and oils were released by the synthesis of glycerine from petroleum products. Similar results have followed the manufacture of synthetic products based on such freely available material as oxygen or nitrogen from air and water; most of our industrial alcohol and many of our solvents are no longer manufactured from cereals, potatoes, or other farm produce, which can now be added to the available food supply.

At present, oil furnishes the basis for most of the cheap raw materials used by the organic chemical industry. In the U.S. 90 percent of its products are made from oil, in Europe over 60 percent. This new technology, a gradual development of 19th-century chemistry, inorganic and organic, not only switched production from natural products in many cases but also opened up a new range of drugs and chemicals. A measure is seen in the fact that half the income of the chemical industry now derives from products discovered within the last ten years. Product research in the pharmaceutical industry has thrown on the market hundreds of "miracle" drugs and patent medicines—some of which have come under criticism as being inadequately backed by sufficient medical research. Here technological progress has outrun the controls that are the primary responsibility of the medical profession and the lawmakers.

One advantage of the synthetic materials is purity; they are generally free from the contaminants present in older products made from complex natural raw materials. This has made possible a hitherto unknown consistency in synthetic products. A striking example can be seen in textiles, where synthetic materials virtually have made us independent of natural products. The earlier types of synthetic fibres were manufactured on a cellulose or nitrocellulose base, but these have been superseded by true synthetics, such as nylon, orlon, and dacron, and by-products based on readily available forms of protein, especially casein. These processes led to the development of inexpensive plastics of all sorts, and these have provided excellent substitutes for ceramics, glass, ivory, rubber, and many other materials.

The synthetics are given special qualities for special uses, and natural materials, such as wool or rubber, are usually more versatile than the synthetic materials that have replaced them. For instance, synthetic rubber that outperforms natural rubber in automobile tires is not suitable for other functions where natural rubber still is useful. Thus the natural products are still sustained by something more than sentiment and tradition, although it has to be conceded that with rare exceptions they are losing out wherever they are in direct competition with the laboratory.

Technology for Export

The technology we have discussed was created primarily by response to the challenges of the environment in Western Europe from the 12th century on, and in North America, beginning three centuries later. The difficulties Nature put in the way of Western man have been overcome to a great extent; his material needs have largely been met, and many of his dreams have become realities. The Western nations are proud of these achievements, and tend to parade them before the inhabitants of other parts of the globe, to whom we profess willingness to export our technology so that their standard of living might be raised to the level of our own. Employing this standard, we have come to refer to "backward," or, in less offensive usage, "underdeveloped" countries. Is such a description accurate? If we compare our machines and engineering works with theirs, the answer is an obvious affirmative, but here a second question arises: Is our technology the only possible one, and should every nation on earth go through the same stages of technological development?

In India and China technology very early took a different course from that followed in the West. Recent studies by Sarton, Needham, and others demonstrate that Eastern technology was considerably more advanced than that of the West during the dawning centuries. Cast iron was produced in large quantities in ancient China, drilling for brine was commonly practised, and natural gas was piped to heat the salt pans. Windmills of the Eastern type were harnessed to irrigation wheels. Stirrups were in use, and the collar harness made animal traction superior to anything known in the West. Silk reeling and paper manufacture were well established, and scientific instruments such as the seismograph and the equatorially mounted torque were known. The magnetic compass and the stern rudder were used in navigation.

There is no reason to assume that this advanced technology took a different course in the East because of a sudden lapse of skill or ingenuity. The reason seems to be that Eastern civilizations did not generate the West's faith in the conquest of Nature and so they did not encourage the systematic and continuous effort to understand the universe and its phenomena that has been the hallmark of Western science since the Middle Ages. Joseph Needham notes that "the Supreme Being in China was so soon depersonalized, and lacked the idea of creativity, that it was not obvious that other lesser rational beings could decipher or reformulate the law of a great rational Super-Being by using methods of observation, experiment, hypothesis, and mathematical reasoning." He points out that while Chinese craftsmen were certainly as skilled as their Western counterparts, the rulers were not seriously challenged to develop their products by a progressive merchant class like that the West has known. The Chinese way of life was dominated by Mandarins and the bureaucracy was made up of those who were first of all literati, trained and examined in the classics of ancient China, and tending to look inward and backward.

The great source of wealth in China was the land; it supported a social structure of landlords and tenant farmers, a stabilized, agrarian-based, urban-centred, imperially ruled, and bureaucratically administered society. Although merchants frequently grew wealthy, their status was unstable; they were barred from real influence by custom, and prevented by arbitrary expropriations and selective taxation from forming into a class that might have promoted new advances in technology. Even in the Sung era, when rational classification gave zoology, botany, and chemistry a promising start, the drive soon faltered and failed to lead to full scientific development. In the 14th century, after the Mongols had at last been expelled and north China recovered, the landlords resumed full control.

Everywhere outside the Western world we are confronted with a variety of technological systems that are less machine-dominated and far less pervasive than those that condition our own society. The quality of life in non-Western nations has been determined by philosophical and religious tenets which consign science and technology to a different and less important place. Some aspects of modern life in these civilizations may resemble earlier stages our own world has passed through, but, as Lord Ritchie-Calder recently reminded us, the point is not that "we tried it, but it did not work," but rather to note that in terms of their own culture, "they tried it, and it did work."

For good reasons and bad, we are faced with demands to superimpose our technology on these nations. The case is made that we can avoid a great human disaster only by using modern techniques to overcome the consequences of population explosion and dwindling natural resources. The world, it is pointed out, has grown smaller as a result of our technological progress, and peoples are therefore interdependent. Many of the leaders of the new nations themselves come West to seek advice, counsel, and a share of our material bounty.

The problem is that our technology is far from being culturally neutral. It is a product of Western ideas and value judgments without which many of the impulses guiding it would be meaningless or even destructive. Our technology has served our own development, but it may not fit other peoples' usually more modest demands and resources. We have seen the sudden invasion of Western technology into an ancient culture lead to quick corrosion, to collapse of the class and caste structure on which such a civilization depends. We can point to few successes in synthesizing other cultures and Western methods without yielding to usually disastrous tendencies on both sides to convert them into Western-style technological societies.

Industrialization of underdeveloped countries may have the negative effect of making the small minority of rich people richer and the masses of the poor poorer. One effect of Western technology has been to continually widen the economic gap between the underdeveloped and the developed countries. Its piecemeal introduction elsewhere could create new gaps between more and less developed countries, with obvious political consequences. The planning of any "migration of industrial processes" must take into account the situation that may exist in the new countries over the span of at least a generation. The West is generally committed to the principle that industrialization should aim at a significant rise in the standard of living for all; however, it has not always succeeded in putting the principle into practice at home or abroad.

We must recognize, too, that our modern industries have been developed in such a way they can no longer thrive on local markets alone. Transport facilities linking ever growing markets, an increasingly sophisticated and highly organized flow of goods, even shifts of populations have accompanied the industrialization of the Western world. These questions of scale are all factors that must be taken into account. Otherwise we may shatter the local social structure so suddenly as to recast Blake's "dark Satanic mills" in a new setting, re-creating the kind of industrial misery that occurred in many parts of Europe during the 18th century.

The orderly development of technology in any country has many aspects of natural growth. The simple transfer of modern highly perfected forms of technology is no more possible than it is desirable. The introduction of a technology must provide not only for the first generation of workers and managers but for their successors who will face different needs and potentials. Increasingly our technology must be seen as systems rather than machines, and it requires education rather than mere training—with all that this implies in the way of conflicting values. The very point about modern technology is that it usually eliminates the creative act as the skilled craftsman has mastered it; thus for these latecomers to the Industrial Revolution, as for the weavers and fullers of the 19th-century Midlands, it is not only a man's livelihood but his pride that is at stake.

Is Technology Natural?

New confrontations between developed and underdeveloped nations have been made inescapable by the technological revolution that has shrunk the globe. Thus, in new and urgent ways they raise the old questions about the "unnatural" quality of man's effort to control his environment. Eric Hoffer has written of this phenomenon:

> The mass movements, upheavals and wars which are a by-product of change indicate that the process involves the deeper layers of man's soul. After all, change such as the world has seen during the last hundred years is something wholly unprecedented in human experience. It would be legitimate, therefore, to assume that there is in man's nature a built-in resistance to change. We are not only afraid of the new, but convinced that we cannot really change, that we can adapt ourselves to the new only by getting out of our skin and assuming a new identity. In other words,

drastic change generates a need for a new birth and a new identity. And it perhaps depends upon the way this need is satisfied whether the process of change runs smoothly or is attended with convulsions and explosions.

Man has been meeting and overcoming this resistance to change, and producing a good many convulsions in the process, ever since he began the step-by-step effort to modify the milieu in which he lives. In one sense he was going against Nature, but in another, each technological act that achieved what it was intended to achieve was incorporated into the technological order and became part of the environment natural to man. Mountains, rivers, winds, and streams have always belonged to man's milieu, and, if "natural" means that they were physically manifest and given by Nature, so were the forest fires which provided man's first great instrument for technological change. When, imitating Nature, he took a burning branch and lit his first fire to keep himself warm, he adopted a natural thing to his own ends. Tending and keeping such fires became part of his life, and the home fire thus became natural in another sense.

Using stones and branches as he found them, and then devising new combinations of these natural materials, he gradually made other environment changes. Descending a river on a tree trunk, or a log hollowed out by his new tool, fire, or maybe a raft, was as natural as harnessing the wind to propel his canoe or ship.

If this proposition is sound there is nothing unnatural in the progression that led to a steel ship propelled by twin screws driven by a steam turbine; nor is a man on horseback more natural than a man in a motor car. In each case man, moving step by step, used the forces and forms of Nature to help him master his environment.

The technological segments of man's environment are natural parts of the totality, of the world in which he lives and wants to live. His early artifacts were the product of an intuition which told him that he could combine natural objects in ways that would help him meet the challenges of Nature. There are no natural as opposed to artificial tools. The results of these technological acts are unnatural only in the sense that they were not possible before man invented, constructed, or tamed the means of employing the elemental forces of Nature he has employed to support himself.

The Greeks considered machines and their construction

quite natural. They created a system to reproduce the mechanism of the heavens by complex rotary movements, in which circular movements in all their aspects were studied. Vitruvius described the device:

> Now all machinery is generated by Nature, and the revolution of the universe guides and controls. . . . Since then our fathers had observed this to be so, they took precedents from Nature; imitating them, and led on by what is divine, they developed the comforts of life by their inventions. And so, they rendered some things more convenient by machines and their revolutions, and other things by handy implements. (*De Architectura,* x 1, sec. 4)

From that day to this, the confluence of technological acts has formed a mighty stream, changing man's environment so completely, and in recent years so rapidly, that the rate of change may have become a qualitative factor in itself. The new issues raised by modern technology are more varied than those of the past, and they are accumulating. The freeways, parking lots, airports, and agglomerations of houses may be as natural as the hills, pastures, and streams of our ancestors in the remote past, but they require new and different physical and mental adjustments, and many individuals find no comfort in the statement that this milieu is the product of man's natural effort to meet the challenges of Nature in accordance with his views and beliefs.

As the man-made sectors of human environment grow in importance, technology, rather than being merely an activity of man, partakes more and more of the nature of man. The urge to alter the conditions of life and to improve them in directions of his own choosing is clearly a basic instinct. One may deplore the fact that he has been endowed with some of the means now available for responding to this impulse, but it cannot be denied that technology and the resultant technological order are natural from this point of view as well. Some of the past choices made by the builders of the Western world are certainly regrettable, but few of us would dream of giving up the major technological components of the environment which has become natural to us. It is safe to assume that no modern man would wish to live the way Louis XIV (the richest man of his time) lived at Versailles; there were great privations and discomforts to be endured in exchange for the absence of hurry and haste, noise, and the standardization of many aspects of life. It is, indeed, appropriate to wonder if one who has partaken of modern life would be mentally fit to survive in such an environment —a question, as suggested above, that is not merely a matter of abstract theory in the case of the emerging nations.

Technology is natural from yet another point of view: it still involves obedience to the laws of Nature, even though the mechanistic concept which has governed science since the days of Newton has been abandoned in favour of new theories. Technology's dependence on these laws is emphasized by the growing interdependence between science and technology, which has reached the point where technology is virtually "applied science." Most contemporary technological achievements are based on a logical array of scientifically measured and checked data and facts—all determined in accord with the laws of Nature as defined by science. Technology does not free man in any ultimate sense from the limitations imposed by Nature. All technological achievements arise in the context of Nature and even our most sophisticated inventions are subject to its laws. The signals in our computers cannot pass from one point to another with a speed exceeding that of light, and this sets a natural limit to the number of signals to be transmitted a second, quite apart from the technical fact that the more parts a computer embodies the greater the chances of failure. We may exploit certain laws of Nature in order to derive direct benefit from them or in order to circumvent the limitations set by other laws of Nature, but in any case we remain subject to these laws.

The Liberating Effect

Man's intention in creating artifacts and modifying his environment was to be relieved from oppressive conditions and to enlarge his capabilities and increase his possibilities. As the scope of the arts and crafts expanded, he had at his disposal a constantly widening range of alternatives from which he could choose what he believed to be his destiny.

It cannot be argued that machinery was introduced in antiquity in order to free slaves. But the ultimate decision to abolish slavery in the modern world cannot be divorced from the changes in opinion and practice that were produced by, and in turn helped produce, machine-driven technology. In classical and preclassical civilizations slavery was a recognized institution in the technological order; Roman agronomists regarded animals and slaves as interchangeable "pieces of machinery." This concept was tacitly rejected by the idea of the inherent dignity of man that came with the introduction of Christianity and that opened the way to the use of machines, something which had been dreamt of by generations of frustrated Greek and Roman engineers. In the centuries that followed, the technologists continued to mark their progress by the extent to which their machines replaced human muscles and the manipulation of a craftsman's hands.

In our time the progressive technological improvement in material standards of living, in medical techniques, and in transportation and communication has transcended the original goal of liberation from human drudgery. Nineteenth-century science conceived the idea of the atom as a perpetual-motion machine; in the middle of the 20th century the technologists found ways to liberate atomic energy by fission and fusion processes, and in a sense the old idea is being proved out as we contemplate a technology characterized by the availability of great and possibly even practically unlimited quantities of energy. Already we have all the artificial muscle we require for traditional functions, and technology has moved on to free the human brain from the drudgery of repetitive processes by substituting the logic of the digital computer.

Theoretically at least, it is possible now to visualize a world in which man pays for this liberation by suffering the dominance of a self-sufficient technological system. But this issue, insofar as it partakes of fact instead of romantic fancy, is not new; as technology changed and enlarged his environment man has always had to adjust to the part "given" by Nature and to the technological parts he himself had added.

Technology and Evolution

G. Berber of the *Encyclopédie française* has written:

> The day before yesterday we followed unconsciously what was called Nature; yesterday we tried conscientiously to conform to nature; but today, our power having grown considerably, it behooves us sometimes to protect nature and sometimes to arrange it in ways that seem more favourable. We have somehow become responsible for evolution. . . . A reality is to be constructed, events are no longer to be awaited.

It is true that technology has released man from slavery to subsistence functions, at least in the Western world, and that it has dehumanized much of the work that always occupied him. In the process man has addressed his new skills to projects that may rearrange and even reconstitute Nature—and he has not always done so with full practical or theoretical knowledge of the possible results.

The American Association for the Advancement of Science has warned that "the forces and processes now coming under human control are beginning to match in size and intensity those of nature itself, and our total environment is now subject to human influence. In this situation it becomes imperative to determine that these new powers shall be used for the maximum human good, for if the benefits to be derived from them are great, the possibility of harm is correspondingly serious." Such harm is often irreversible, and where it is not, it requires intense and costly labour to undo the mistakes that have been made.

Western man has been taught that he was given dominion over the earth, and that it is his duty to use nature, not to abstain from using it. To date, man's uses still outweigh his abuses, and he is still reminded by occasional displays of nature's forces in storms, landslides, earthquakes, or volcanic eruptions that his dominion is somewhat less than complete. Whether technological inroads into nature's domain really have materially affected patterns of natural evolution is still an open question.

From the earliest days of *Homo faber,* technology has stored information in its artifacts and handed down its methods, and it is quite possible that this may have accelerated evolution in some ways. However, technology has developed on a grand scale only in the Western world, and it is highly doubtful that a case could be made that these machine-minded Westerners have evolved into a species or subspecies different in any fundamental sense from those who have not adopted the Western mode of life and may not even consider it viable.

The most serious concerns aroused by technology stem from the accelerating rate of change that has marked the contemporary era. J. Robert Oppenheimer, the distinguished physicist who headed Princeton's Institute for Advanced Study, wrote:

> This world of ours is a new world, in which the unity of knowledge, the nature of human communities, the order of society, the order of ideas, the very notions of society and culture have changed, and will not return to what they have been in the past. What is new is new not because it has never been there before, but because it has changed in quality. . . . One thing that is new is the prevalence of newness, the changing scale and scope of change itself, so that the world alters as we walk in it, so that the years of man's life measure not some small growth or rearrangement or moderation of what he learned in childhood, but a great upheaval.

Really important technological innovations were rare in the past; until very recent times no more than one or two changes of any magnitude occurred in a man's lifetime, and it often required the passage of generations before scientific discoveries were converted into technological applications. As science and technology became more closely interwoven during this century the rate of change increased significantly. There were only seven years between the recognition that the atomic bomb was a theoretical possibility and its use at Hiroshima. Only three years (1948-51) elapsed between the invention in December 1947 and the sale of the first transistors.[3] The invention-to-production period of the solar battery (1953-55) and of stereo-specific rubbers and plastics (1955-58) likewise was only three years.

[3] It may be argued, of course, that the history of semiconductors goes back more than a generation.

It is natural that fears should arise that this accelerated rate of change might entail a loss of control over technology and constitute a serious threat to human freedom. These fears can be extrapolated into panic by those who suggest that the rate will continue to accelerate and that technology will spread with bewildering rapidity and in unprecedented volume and variety over the entire surface of the earth. There is much evidence, however, to suggest, on the contrary, that there is an upper limit, somewhere, inherent in the very nature of man. And this applies not only to production and consumption but also to the rate of change.

Man is not only free to choose his technology; he can also control the rate at which it absorbs previously human functions. The time spans cited above to demonstrate the rapid rate of change can be understood in another sense; under the compulsions of war effort it was demonstrated at Hiroshima that atomic energy could be released through fission or fusion reactions; in the absence of any similar compulsion the development of atomic power plants has been slow and desultory. In the case of the latest marvel, the computer, the application has been erratic, with the technological potential often counterbalanced by such social considerations as unemployment resulting from automated industrial processes. Some of the excitement and apprehension aroused by the new systems technology may result from its special impact on other orders, notably education, politics, and law, which until now have had little direct contact with technology.

Technology and Science

Cooperation between technology and science in the modern manner began in Germany about a century ago. Extensive laboratory research was efficiently organized for the first time and began to regularly produce practical as opposed to theoretical results. This success spread the new research techniques to other countries with a similar concern about technical problems.

When, at the end of the century, Russia belatedly embarked on a drive for industrialization, the Minister of Finance, Sergei Witte, directed the universities to undertake research on the problems and possibilities of the rising petroleum industry, while, remarkably enough, the lavish petroleum industry of the United States, until World War I, continued to rely primarily on practical technological experience.

The growth of industrial research was facilitated by demonstration that improved technology produced direct and often rapid economic returns. This tended to emphasize the characteristic differences between the type of laboratory work on which science had been based in the past, called "pure" or "fundamental" research, and the "applied" research needed to solve technological problems.

Scientific research deals with a set of puzzles; some of these are sorted out and solved as the work proceeds, but certain unsolved anomalies remain—observations and data which cannot be fitted in with generally accepted theory. As their number grows, a crisis may occur, and this scientific "revolution," overthrowing the accepted paradigms, will lead to another, wider theory, which then has to be confirmed by further research and experiments suggested by the new paradigms. By contrast, the applied researcher aims at a limited and clearly defined goal.

Technological research started centuries ago in the workshops of the craftsmen as a continuing experimental effort to overcome the operational difficulties encountered in handling and fabricating raw materials. Without support by scientific knowledge of the phenomena underlying these techniques, such research proceeded entirely by trial and error. With the gradual development of the science of applied mechanics during the 18th century the technical innovators began to draw upon basic data supplied by the scientist—and thus began the process of deliberate as opposed to fortuitous invention.

Deliberate inventions, contrived in response to the economic and technical demands of their time, can be traced back to the early Middle Ages. But it was the joining of technical skill and scientific knowledge that permitted invention to be truly directed. This development has had a profound effect on the position of the inventor, who was once the darling of technological society. Realization of the ideas of an individual technical innovator now demands a team of scientists and engineers and financial support of considerable magnitude. Thus most modern research and development—R & D in the current alphabetical jargon—has passed to the provinces of private corporations and government, which have the capacity to organize and support large-scale teamwork. Although it is still true that the basic elements of invention are opportunity, need, and genius, these are rarely joined today in the private workshop of the lonely inventor.

A new type of scientist-turned-inventor-turned-engineer holds the key to the technology of the future; he provides the connecting link between science and technology. But no matter how closely this connection is made, technological invention is not simply a matter of logic, reason, and experience devoid of the intuition and inspiration deemed to guide the artist. No discovery has ever been made solely by logical deduction, nor has any work of art been produced without calculating craftsmanship. The subconscious is at work in both cases, and technological achievement still requires a creative act.

The impact of science on technology has its counterpart in the impact of technology on scientific research. Thus the methods and techniques of the engineering sciences are now applied in practically all the biological sciences, and more particularly in human biology and medicine. The new discipline of "bio-engineering" examines the major processes occurring within and around living material, such as cells, in terms of engineering concepts. This analysis and the building of analogues give us further insight into life processes.

The Systematic Concept

It is obvious that the development of operations research, systems engineering, and the possibilities opened up by servomechanisms and computers in technological research and application have greatly increased the complexity of contemporary technology.

Systems engineering is the sophisticated development of the older time and motion studies aimed at a more rational division of work between machine and hand. Every step in an operation is defined and analyzed in relation to other operations belonging to the same chain. In this way models are constructed, and with their help it is determined whether certain tasks, manual or intellectual, can profitably be automated and whether there are sub-tasks which should not be automated. Computers have added new dimensions to this process.

Decision-making mathematics (dynamic and linear programming) is used in conjunction with automated machinery to direct the manufacturing process at certain selected points, thus entirely eliminating the judgment of the human operator who formerly had to check the operation. An elaborate version of the same type of decision-making is applied to industrial planning. Sound decision-making in any event must be based on timely and well-selected information about the crucial factors governing the problem at issue. The more timely and the better selected such information is, the less general experience or guesswork goes into the decision. Data processing systems, with their infallible memories and their ability to store and instantly retrieve vast arrays of facts and figures, hence have become tools employed by executives in making major decisions affecting broad areas of operation in industry and government. This may involve production, inventory marketing, manpower and transportation problems, and even military strategy.

If, for example, factory expansion or production needs are under discussion, computers can furnish management with the calculated economic effects of several alternative expansion plans, including supplies of raw materials, their transportation and that of the end products, as well as market demand. Or they can provide a defense minister with the exact location of his forces and instant calculations on what would be required to re-deploy them.

Complex techniques of simulation are required in these operations, and these involve the creation of an artificial situation having all the characteristics of a real one—an imitation of experience with mathematical models. A basic operation is thus set up, and coded information representing the various forces that might act upon it are fed into the computer. The research worker then studies the effects of these forces; he can fly to the moon without ever leaving the ground, and such flights have become commonplace in the new technology which determined in advance and with great precision what man would encounter and how he would react when he finally penetrated outer space. Here the computers are performing functions of the human brain that go beyond mere memory, although they have not yet attained the flexibility and the subtle gradation of even the simplest kind of rational thought.

Consequences of Automation

The consequences of automation in industry are various and complex, aside from the effect on society of such manifestations as displaced human workers. In absorbing the previous functions of manual labour, and translating into machine language even those smaller corrective measures which were formerly taken by workers with high skills, the systems have to be adapted to a rigid, mechanical logic. This is a highly complicated technological process which creates new internal problems even as it yields great advantages. While the products of automated industries are closer to desired standards and the errors inevitable in human operations are eliminated, it is often more difficult to change these automated assembly lines to suit special demands. Changing over to a better or a new type of product requires complicated replanning. Automation thus can produce a tendency toward standardization and stagnation. Among those who are displaced or removed from direct association with the process may be men with a more intimate knowledge and intuitive feel for the product than that of the analysts or the designers of the automated machinery. In the sense that the technological act is not simply the sum of a series of operations, technology may eliminate a component of cumulative experience that could have serious consequences for its own future development. Modern technology still shows some traces of the old crafts from which it was born; its logic seems to demand, however, that these be finally eliminated, and the great question may be, as Ellul suggests, whether the creative act may not go with them.

Complexity is a feature characterizing practically every aspect of modern life. In technology as in science this has produced a trend toward specialization that has accelerated as the mathematico-logical structure on which it was founded expanded. Until about 1850, the principles on which the older technology was based were still within the ready grasp of the uninitiated, and skilled workers could change jobs within a wide range of options without too much difficulty, except for a brief period of readapting. Even at the turn of the century a military engineer was regarded as the equivalent of a civil engineer, and he could easily leave the army and take up civilian work. Now the specialization and complexity of the branches and sub-branches within a field of technology have become such that each new level of attainment—and it often takes a lifetime to reach it—presents an ascending order of intrinsic complexities.

The technological act is growing so difficult to understand, even for the insider, that its consequences, intended or unintended, are becoming more difficult to forecast. As technology is called upon to fulfill a social or economic function, a number of outsiders must be involved with the insiders in decision-making. But the outsider is bound to be perplexed by the mysteries of technique, while the number of insiders who really understand the larger implications of the technological act tends to be reduced by the narrowing demands of a complex discipline. It has been said that a man who learns to be an engineer, and stays abreast of his rapidly changing specialty, hasn't time to learn anything else.

The Military Model

Military engineering, if that once simple and limited term can still apply to the vast array of technological appurtenances to modern armed forces, is perhaps the prime example of how the technological act has consequences that go far beyond technology itself. It all began with the employment of engineering skill in the building of bridges, palisades, and fortresses, the construction of naval vessels, and the development of armament. Siege machinery perfected by the Assyrians and the horsedrawn military equipage of Greek and Roman times remained essentially unchanged even after the invention of gunpowder, except for a few details of construction. The really basic changes date from World War I, which saw the displacement of cavalry by tanks and airplanes. In the years that followed what had been regarded as ultimate principles of tactics and strategy gave way to the requirements and the possibilities of the new military hardware.

Mechanization of military strategy was completed in the course of World War II. It was the first war in which fighting was three-dimensional, based on a new technology in which detection devices, rockets, and missiles had an important part. The pace of technological development was speeded up by the advent of the atomic bomb, of which Ritchie Calder has said "the safe breakers forced the lock of the atom before the locksmiths knew how it worked." This has been followed by the intercontinental ballistic missile to carry the atomic warhead without the touch of a human hand except that required to push the launching button. A new strategy of military deterrence has emerged which makes armies, navies, and even air forces obsolete. The voracious demands of this new military technology, spurred by the competition of a Cold War now a generation old, dominates research and development in both West and East. The launching of satellites and space probes—even the "moon landings"—are the direct product of the military impulse. Some experts claim that we are only at the beginning of this development and that the influence of military technology will become more important in the future. Others wonder whether there can be any end this side of global suicide for a technological competition that already has contributed to our vocabulary the term "overkill"—meaning that our weapons provide a destructive capacity considerably beyond that required to destroy mankind *in toto*.

Apart from their scientific and technological implications, these developments obviously have powerful political, cultural, economic, and psychological effects. The citizens of this modern world, even where they theoretically have the right to do so, find it difficult to decide whether huge sums of tax money should be spent on these vast projects which threaten to destroy them even as they purport to protect them. The armament race itself has become an aspect of "psychological warfare"; and our military hardware often seems to take the form of status symbols rather than reflecting realistic projections of sound strategic decisions. The "space race" has caused thoughtful men to wonder whether we are collectively being shoved into the position of the adventurer who explained that he climbed the mountain because it was there. What of priorities? Does it make sense to spend our substance on a trip to the moon while a substantial portion of mankind still faces starvation? Are we actually improving our strategic position when we increase our capacity for military destruction with means that might be devoted to containing the spreading flames of what Adlai Stevenson called "the revolution of rising expectations"?

These developments of military engineering demonstrate the terrifying impact technology could have on our Western world. The technologist can only argue in defense of his art that his creative act produces an end that is neither good nor bad. Technological problems, like those of science, recognize only a correct or an incorrect solution; the value judgments of "good" or "bad" come only when the solution is applied to the affairs of men. It is as a social and political animal that the technologist is required to ask himself whether his particular technological act is necessary to the common good and whether the application of his skills may produce unintended consequences along with the good or neutral results he can readily foresee.

The technological imperative arises from the possibilities and impulses leading to further applications. Improvements, embodied in a technological act, like solutions to scientific problems, always raise further queries and problems. It is in the sense that man's relationship with his technology is natural, the result of the purposeful activity of *Homo faber,* that this imperative will remain with him.

PART THREE

MILIEU AND MAN

IN THE WEST, the technological order must be reckoned as all-pervasive; in the rest of the world it is knocking at the door or already stepping in. New human issues arise from the confrontation of the older orders of man's existence by this creation of materials, processes, and techniques; old issues must be restated in terms of technology's new demands.

In a sense the dichotomy between the "two cultures," in the term grown common since C. P. Snow employed it in his Rede Lecture of 1959, is the technological order against the rest. Snow addressed himself particularly to the specialization within each academic subject and the lack of contact between faculties and students. In many cases science and technology are taught at special, separate institutions; a comparable isolation often grows up on conventional campuses. Many of the older universities traditionally looked askance at science, whether pure or applied, and long hesitated to include it in their curriculum. If science has not generally gained the aura of academic respectability, it is technology, with its inescapable material overtones, that has taken its place beyond the pale.

In his *Act of Creation* Arthur Koestler described the dichotomy in the following passage:

> . . . the average educated person will be reluctant to admit that a work of art is beyond the level of his comprehension; but he will in the same breath and with a certain pride confess his complete ignorance of the principles which make his radio work, the forces which make the stars go round, the factors which determine the heredity of his children, and the location of his own viscera and glands.
>
> One of the consequences of this attitude is that he utilizes

> the products of science and technology in a purely possessive, exploitive manner without comprehension or feeling. His relationship to the objects of his daily use, the tap which supplies his bath, the pipes which keep him warm, the switch which turns on the light—in a word, to the environment in which he lives, is impersonal and possessive—like the capitalist's attitude to his bank account, not the art collector's to his treasures which he cherishes because he "understands" them. . . . Modern man lives isolated in his artificial environment, not because the artificial is evil as such, but because of his lack of comprehension of the forces which make it work—of the principles which relate his gadgets to the forces of nature, to the universal order. It is not central heating which makes his existence "unnatural," but his refusal to take an interest in the principles behind it. By being entirely dependent on science, yet closing his mind to it, he leads the life of an urban barbarian.[1]

The situation is aggravated by the fact that specialization leads to the use of more and more jargon. Even within the same branch of science, the specialists hardly understand each other's language and the technologist and the humanist use the same idiom only on rare occasions—almost never outside their frustrating efforts at professional interchange.

These misunderstandings are perpetuated and propagated by the manner in which scientific and technical subjects are commonly presented to the lay public. The extreme of popular "science fiction," which is usually an extrapolation of the technologically possible, may be amusing and thrilling. But only the technologist will be able to judge where the author has made his own "jump into imagination" from the real train of reasoning based on technical facts. Those without scientific training may find that the fiction compounds the false hopes and false fears usually engendered by the unknown.

Similar confusion is caused by the sensational and undigested information often published by the press in regard to technological or scientific achievements and problems. Few journalists are adequately trained to deal with these matters, and one result is a common misapplication of terms that do not belong to the world of science or technology. The use of "memory" or similar names denoting human faculties for parts of a computer has helped to spread mistaken notions about these new machines and to

[1] The Macmillan Company, New York, 1964; Hutchinson & Co. Ltd., London.

lead many people to endow them with mysterious, human powers. The term "data storage unit" instead of "memory" would have described the computer function correctly and neutrally.

A good deal of modern technology (and especially science) can be understood properly only if the discussion is kept at a level attained only by specialized education; "popularization" therefore, when it is actually possible, is an act akin to translation and requires the writer to be a master of both the source language and the idiom in which he is working. The Editor of the *Oxford Mail* noted in this regard: "The circumstances certainly are special, for on most newspaper staffs there is no one who can be sure that a science (or technology) story is either sense or nonsense; it is taken in completely blind faith. That is surely the kind of gamble no editor would tolerate with politics or sport."

This "language barrier" has confronted technologist and humanist (both presumably aware of the need for cooperation) with a number of false problems, some of which have been mentioned earlier. Two of these deserve detailed discussion.

The most extreme of current philosophical theses holds that modern man is somehow "committed" to technology, which has developed in a totally autonomous way capable of painlessly enslaving mankind. Jacques Ellul argues the case in *The Technological Society*. Here he states that *technique* (by which he means the technological order rather than technology) has supplanted Nature as the *milieu* of modern man. This milieu is then said to be (a) artificial; (b) autonomous; (c) self-determining; (d) growing according to a causal process, which (e) sets means over ends, so that (f) all parts are mutually implicated to such a degree that no technical problem can be isolated any longer from the technological order as such. John Wilkinson, the American philosopher-mathematician who translated Ellul's work into English, has given this summary of his central thesis:

> Men, argued Ellul, had become slaves of their erstwhile servant. To use Nietzsche's terms, the necessary reassessment of value would signify that the means-end relationship had been reversed by technology; that man was no longer *the* end-in-itself of religion and philosophy but had become the material substratum of the industrial ma-

> chinery; that is, the means by which the new social order is being realized.[2]

Few, if any, technologists would accept this construct, offered by a distinguished academician trained in law and sociology. Here Blake's "dark Satanic mills" are no longer a poetic fancy; Ellul seems to endow *La Technique* not only with anthropomorphic but with demonological attributes. It is, of course, the burden of the present author's preceding exposition that technology does *not* have such internal dynamism and is wholly incapable of setting its own rules on the basis of its own logic within a completely closed circle. Many examples have been given here to show how technology deals with the questions that are put to it; these may arise from the imperfection of its own former achievements or they may represent impulses from outside technology. When, in the early days of the last century, there was a growing need for quicker means of transporting people and industrial products between manufacturing centres and shipping ports, vehicles of various types were invented to supplant the mail coach and the wagon. In central England the canal system was improved; steam-driven railway trains followed; and then the variety of vehicles made possible by the development of internal-combustion prime movers. This process was attended by dislocations from beginning to end; banes accompanied the boons of quicker and more efficient transportation, and they still do, now that men are taking to the skies in supersonic jet aircraft. But all of these problems, from a strictly technological point of view, could be solved or avoided. They must be blamed on the *hubris* of mankind.

Nor does every technological achievement carry within itself the imperative toward a further step. Mankind has selected an array of technologies that currently form its technological order, but has ignored others which continue to lie dormant. Undoubtedly we will drop some technologies now in use, and thus change still further the existing technological order, which in fact is necessarily in flux as it responds to the changing needs of mankind for building the habitat it desires or aspires to. Technology has become a calculated and intentional application of scientific principles and data or "natural laws," in ways determined by

[2] Ellul, op. cit.

smaller or larger groups of men responsible for social, political, and economic policymaking. We may quarrel about the size and composition of such groups and about the nature and quality of the policymaking; but these can hardly be considered as technological issues.

To indict the technological order for ushering in the age of nuclear terror, as is popularly done, is to ignore the nature of the decision to make the first atomic bomb—to rip it out of the context of world war where national survival was realistically in question. We may doubt today—as some people did even at the moment of the decision—whether the atomic bomb really shortened the war and whether future risks should not have been seen to outweigh momentary advantages. But here again, the critical decisions were made in the political order. Scientists opened the possibilities because of an abstract interest in the phenomena which long predated any consideration of using this source of energy to destroy their fellowmen. The technologists came forward to make the weapon in the spirit other men offered to kill, and be killed, in the service of an embattled civilization.

The political order tends to single out and magnify certain technological achievements under the doubtful rubric of national prestige; similarly the economic order may produce great pressure for technological change for competitive reasons. In some cases these work together, in some they cancel each other—as appears to have been the case with the Mach 3 airplane, where political considerations overcame the economic forces working for delay in introduction of the great advance in speed of air transport.

The space program has certainly enriched technology and science with many data and techniques that may be useful in other fields, but again it seems to have drawn its motive force primarily from groups outside technology. A statement made in the U.S. House of Representatives, gave the program credit for producing "a strengthened national economy, new jobs and job categories, better living, fresh consumer goods, improved education, increased health, stimulated business enterprise and a host of long-range values which may ultimately make the immediate benefits pale into relative insignificance." This glowing recitation hardly seems justified by the facts of the case, but the nature of the argument makes it clear that the technologist is being required to adapt his techniques to the requirements of national policymakers, who have much on their minds beyond indulging the happy band of space researchers and technicians who may very well want to shoot the moon just to see if they can.

Decisions on Technology

While it is clearly possible for political or other groups to direct technological developments, they must deal with real technical possibilities, and these can only be determined within the technological order. Thus the rules for technology are laid down both by *Nature* and by *Homo faber*. In this sense, technological problems do not arise in the manner of scientific problems, where an inner logic and structure of scientific theory based on certain axioms unfolds. Technology, now receiving a strong impulse from science, still moves along lines very different from those traced by the progress of physics or chemistry, where man extends the range of his knowledge systematically, on the basis of axioms and hypotheses which have so far helped him to understand the structure of the matter he is investigating. Technology lacks such an inner structure to support its future developments. The technologist's operating theory is actually a pragmatic means of meeting needs arising from man's habitat; these very human matters are his "imperative." There is only a technology of the present, limited by the decisions of external policymakers.

It is rare indeed that the voters of a democratic society are presented, formally or informally, with an issue that is purely an outgrowth of technology. Even though the technological implications may be great, as in the case of the Mach 3 airplane, the problems come before the people wrapped in economic, sociological, or political considerations not different in kind from those traditionally passed on by the electorate. A century ago the people of the United States supported the decision of the government to provide land grants to help finance railroads into the interior; the elements of that earlier decision were repeated in the matter of federal subsidy for development of a new system of supersonic transport, and the implications are not likely to be more revolutionary than the westward progress of the "iron horse."

Those who deplore the lack of control over technological development are by implication saying that we need to find a way to halt and perhaps reverse the thrust of human history. Each generation creates its own technology as part of its way of life, its culture. It is unhistorical to believe that a society can somehow return to the simpler past while retaining the complex advantages of the technological present. To do so man would have to accept all the conditions of the past, including the standing rules of a more primitive society and its government. Such visions, of course, are utopian.

The second proposition of Ellul, that man is losing or has already lost his freedom to technology, contains both truth and error. If we reject the Ellulian contention that technology has acquired an autonomous force, the technologies which grace and spoil our lives may be taken as evidence that man is still in control, but, as so often in the past, has done himself both good and harm in his contest with his environment.

The freedoms we have lost must be reckoned against those we have gained if we are to strike a proper balance. There is an element of freedom in the technological expansion of the ranges of choice; modern man may travel from New York to San Francisco by foot, horseback, bicycle, automobile, train, ship, bus, or plane. All the possibilities past the first one have been added by technology. And not only have the new technological entries vastly shortened the time required by the journey, they have greatly reduced its cost. Both developments have combined to make the journey a real possibility for most Americans, while only a generation ago it was possible only for the rich or the adventurous. This new mobility is certainly a measure of freedom; but it is also the root cause of the great surge of urbanization which is a great phenomenon of the 20th century, and the resultant congestion of our cities is certainly reducing the freedoms as well as the amenities of those who are required by our social-political-economic system to live in them. Those who do not accept Ellul's dark vision can only say that the real argument still turns on the view of human nature. If toolmaking is accepted as a fundamental human characteristic, as it seems to be even from the narrowest biological view, then technology is an inescapable part of the human condition, as benign and as malevolent as man himself.

The Physical Limits

Certain limits are set to technology by the very fact that man is a living animal with limitations of a bodily and sensory nature. This condition determines what he can do with machines, and it still applies even to the ultimate tool he has now devised: automatic production and computation directed by electronic computers.

In this century technology has established links to the social sciences as well as those that provide the theoretical base required by its hardware. The study of people at work has expanded to include the whole range of relations between management and workers, and among workers themselves; the sense of "belonging," and of the human worth of the collective enterprise, is accepted as a component of technology's creative act. This, in part, is the area of what has come to be called labour relations, or industrial psychology, but the direct relation between machine and man belongs to ergonomics, sometimes also called engineering psychology, or human factors engineering. Ergonomics originally was concerned with such matters as the design of machinery, so that the operational parts of the machine harmonized with the human body, thus increasing efficiency and making for reliability and safety. Now the science extends to the study and breakdown of existing jobs and new tasks and the design of machinery that not only supplements but may also replace the human body and mind.

Although studies of this kind have only begun to yield their first results, they are already encountering limitations wholly aside from those imposed by the laws of nature. Oppenheimer said in his first Whidden Lecture in 1962:

> . . . the scientific knowledge which may be available to men—not much today–will always be, as in our knowledge of the physical world, very, very incomplete and partial, and that the sense of having to live and act in response to tradition, good judgement, and wisdom, which

> we have now, will not ever be alleviated by any development of the sciences. I think we need secondly to remember that a great part of the present scene arises not from what we have learned, but by its application in technology. This, in turn, rests on an organization of the economy and to a more limited, but still real, extent on our political arrangements. Neither of these derives from, nor is in any tight way related to, the sciences, because, although the growth of knowledge is largely responsive to human needs, it is not fully so.[3]

We actually know very little about the manner in which man's environment, as altered by his advancing technology, may have affected him as a biological species. In this sense some of the most impassioned arguments over the effects of what might be loosely called our man-made "evolution" over the last few generations take place in a scientific vacuum. The progress of medicine and pharmaceutical science and increasing emphasis on measures of public hygiene and safety certainly have made man's life far less risky than it was in previous times. In the technologically advanced West we live longer and are much healthier, in physical terms at least. But there are as yet few data to show whether modern amenities like air-conditioning, central heating, etc., have had long-range influence on the general condition of health, and whether this new "conditioned" life may not be a source of biological mutation. There are many who claim to identify major psychic consequences of the tremendous acceleration of the rhythm of life in the West. Although there is little agreement on their meaning, there seem to be demonstrable psychological effects of the over-organization, regulation, and bureaucratization that have inescapably accompanied the advance of technology. The question has been raised, and not ironically, as to whether man has finally been "domesticated" by his own creations.

Historically, much of our modern technology may be seen as an expression of individuality at the personal level by questing and ambitious man; and of nationality at the collective level, which harnessed the technological process to military and economic competition. Survival of these impulses, whether they are seen as good or bad, becomes a real issue as technology becomes ever more pervasive and dehumanized. In the West we have entered an age in

[3] J. Robert Oppenheimer, *The Flying Trapeze: Three Crises for Physicists*, Oxford University Press, London, 1964, pp. 2–3.

which control of the technological system has become more important than the simple exploitation of technology, which was the traditional source of its vitality.

We may assume that man will remain both *Homo faber* and *Homo ludens,* a tinkerer playing with ideas and mechanisms. If those impulses disappear he will cease to be a human being according to any definition available to us now. The danger would not appear to be imminent, since we are hardly in sight of the end of technology's irreplaceable role in the elevation and self-realization of mankind. We have hardly run out of opportunities for *Homo faber* to employ his skills. The world at large has an urgent need for the energy, materials, and human ingenuity being made surplus in the West by technology. At many points along the long road to the 20th century it was claimed that the end of technology was approaching. But this "end" has been like an ever receding horizon, pulling back before recurrent waves of faith in, and fear of, new technological possibilities. Across the centuries we hear today echoes of Dr. Johnson's famous declamation: "The age is running mad after innovation. All the business of the world is to be done in a new way; men are to be hanged in a new way; Tyburn itself is not safe from the fury of innovation."

The Economic Consequences

Money and machines always have been closely related, but their contacts were of widely varying kinds over past centuries. Technology, while it was still limited to arts and crafts, was tied to the local or at most regional economy, up to the days of the Roman Empire. Ancient trade was almost entirely concerned with agricultural produce: corn, wine, and olive oil were the bulk goods of antiquity. Thales of Miletus, the philosopher, could corner the market by hiring all the olive presses in advance when he foresaw a rich harvest of olives, but such chances for wholesale economic operations were few and far between. Even the trade in luxury goods of the Roman Empire was very limited, and it developed no significant new technology.

The growth of towns and cities during the Middle Ages, and the rise of their middle-class inhabitants, became the dominant factor in a new and increasingly complex economic system. Access to foreign markets helped the skilled craftsmen find ready customers for their products. The increased possibilities for profit interested merchants and bankers not only in the end product and the sources of the raw materials but in production itself. They began to invest in the machinery the craftsmen needed to produce more goods. This pattern of financing technological applications to industry and commerce emerged with the dominant medieval crafts and has continued to this day, with the added variation of comparable capital formation by the state in socialist regimes.

The opening of new overseas markets, the advent of new raw materials, and the outburst of creative invention during the 18th century forged the modern bonds that link technology and economics. In the next century the factory replaced the craftsmen's guilds, and mass production began to require mass money to finance the requirements of raw materials, new sources of energy, and overseas markets for mass-produced goods.

For a time, toward the end of the 19th century, the capitalist entrepreneur and the market mechanisms were presumed to be able to meet all the economic problems the factory technology was likely to create with its swelling stream of goods. The political order in the West was enjoined to *laissez faire,* and for a while it did seem as though governments could stand aside while miracles of organization, production, and distribution were performed by the untrammeled working of supply and demand. This illusion did not last long. It quickly became evident that the new technology was pushing modern industry beyond its local limits; it was, as it has remained, an international force, destructive in war, creative in peace.

The international thrust of the economic order required technology to provide rapid and universal transport and communication, and provided the means for achieving it. The process has continued ever since. The comparatively small "family" of factory owners of the last century, who usually functioned in a highly individualistic way as unofficial princes of the realm, have disappeared into huge industrial complexes with hired managers who operate as prime ministers beholden to stockholders, labour unions, banks, and various agencies of government. The operations of these great combines are the very fabric of national and international economy and the object of intensive public scrutiny and concern: at the Santa Barbara Conference on the Technological Order in 1962 it was said that "in America the Small Businessman entered the Gallery of the Heroes in the niche next to the Small Farmer; the Big Businessman entered the Hall of the Gods."

Aldous Huxley once wrote: "The Industrial Revolution brought the vice of speed." Technology provides the means of meeting the demands of this vice—whether it be to transport executives around the world in jet planes, hook far-flung operations together by wire or airborne message systems, or, most recently, provide instantaneous access to vast collections of data through computers. These gadgets are the nervous system of the gigantic body of production and processing machinery that is the modern base of the economic order.

The development of decision-making theory and techniques for handling the present "information avalanche" is becoming more and more important, for it may well be only here that the economic order encounters real limits to its growth and adaptation. A highly complex infra- and superstructure is already required to maintain, improve, control, and distribute the products and services of the economic order, and technologists rather than economists or managerial experts are required for key executive roles.

This has given rise to a theory that technology is due to dominate the economy in the foreseeable future, as it breeds complexity in both micro- and macroeconomics. This tends to make macroeconomy into a planned and regulated mass economy rather than an aggregation of microeconomics. Technological development, it is contended, tends to press economies into its service as a social technique for the rationalization of the economic conditions which technology itself creates and requires. Thus the economy is absorbed into an amorphous technological system. This is the basic argument of the "technocrats," who contend that economics has been so complicated by technology it cannot be understood by the average citizen and his political leaders and therefore should be turned over to engineers and scientists who can properly evaluate and control its pervasive impact on all aspects of human life.

The technocrats reject the experience that has always plagued the economist, who has tried to apply the exact measurements of mathematics to human affairs, and has repeatedly found that man is a most unaccountable animal who does not act according to quantitative laws. The effort of econometrics to rationalize all processes encounters the fact that the material on which it bases its calculations consists of masses of individuals whose reactions are not always rational. The effort to control the human element goes on, however, with varying success.

The effort to bring technology into play to shape the economic choices of men has produced a major invasion of consumer markets by advertising. Using the latest technological devices and the methods of applied psychology to attract men to goods and services has become a common practice throughout the West in this century. Advertising may serve legitimate functions in spreading the use of new products and alerting consumers to an expanding range of choices. But it also can be used to distort values, conceal defects, and divert consumers from more socially valuable goods. Also it may even create what amounts to artificial markets by stimulating desire for new goods or new models that embody no significant technical improvements over those already in service. In the automobile industry this kind of "planned obsolescence" is the basis of the steadily rising sales curves that continue despite theoretical saturation of American markets.

The manipulation of demand through advertising is not the only way in which the technologists have joined with economists in producing planned and inadvertent results of great consequence to the market. The pressure of the economic order for reducing production costs and the technological order's response in labour-saving devices has produced a situation in which a full-production economy is no longer a full-employment economy. Aside from the social and political consequences of what has been called "structural unemployment," this begins to have profound implications for the traditional market concepts based on scarcity. Technology in effect is creating a new leisure class, made up not of wealthy aristocrats but of unskilled, and increasingly of skilled, workers no longer needed to man the few posts required for the control of automatic factories and computerized offices. The problem is not likely to yield to a simple choice between slowing down automation or upgrading workers, since political pressures constantly remind the economic planners that human capital is not the same as financial capital.

The technologist is bound to play some minor role in the solution of this new "leisure problem." But it seems unlikely that he and the economist are going to be permitted to go it alone as they did for a time after Adam Smith proclaimed a Western faith in an "invisible hand" that ordered economic affairs and took care of the social consequences of the invading technology. The hands required to straighten out current technological dislocations will be highly visible, and they will be found in several orders.

Technology and Politics

For many generations technological change has been manifest in a steady accretion of law—patents to protect the rights of inventors, traffic regulations to control the passage of vehicles, labour legislation to protect the rights of the men who operate the machines, statutes aimed at conserving natural resources and checking industrial pollution of air and water, and now the imponderables raised by manned satellites which have forced the lawyers to turn their attention to something called Space Law.

This body of law represents one response of the political order to technology. But this is only the more stable and orderly part of the reaction that has followed as technology served to concentrate and redistribute political power in patterns unknown in the days when men were ruled by Divine Right, or military force, or a combination of the two.

The technologist has always been indispensable to public works and to private prosperity. In modern times he has created systems which bring the public and private sectors of human activity together in ways that are often determinants of political and social forms. Karl Marx taught that technological development had created a socioeconomic imperative for the public ownership and control of all the means of production for human needs. Great modern states have come into being on this principle, and the supreme peril of the age—atomic warfare—results from the confrontation of the older industrial powers by this new ideology, with its obvious attractions for the nations of the underdeveloped world.

Even in the most conservative of industrial states technology has steadily expanded government activity in fields once left exclusively to the private entrepreneurs. Where factories continue to be privately owned, standards for production may be set by government regulation, and the public planners may even determine the allocation of resources to the industry, the wages it must pay, and the prices it may charge. The axiom seems to be that the more technological society becomes, the more the state is forced to exercise control over technological activities, while science and technology themselves provide the state with increasing possibilities and facilites for such control. Many in the West deplore the increase of bureaucracy this entails and the real and apparent limitations on traditional freedoms, but no developing democratic culture has escaped the process. The effect has been to accentuate the importance of political issues that go back to antiquity. Now, as then, the need is for institutions and processes that guarantee that the decisions taken to govern our social development are taken in the common good. Technology has broadened the politician's choice, and all too often also has obscured his view.

History makes it clear that man's ability as a technological inventor frequently outstrips his capacity to use his inventions wisely. Thus a critical role necessarily devolves upon the political order, which might properly be described as a master technology charged with guaranteeing that technological achievements are absorbed in society in ways that contribute to its stability and general well-being.

As technology reaches into nearly every field of human activity, government cannot avoid expanding its own reach. At the same time the very complexity of technology seems to be reducing the number of people able to understand its phenomena adequately in terms of its impact on society. If our political leadership failed at every stage of development to make adequate provision for the changes brought by the automobile over half a century, how will it handle the advent of supersonic aircraft which make their way from drawing board to runway in a matter of a year or two?

By design in the Communist countries, almost inadvertently in the West, the basic resources of science and technology are already under some degree of public control.

Almost all major scientific research takes place in government or university laboratories and research stations. Directly or indirectly the public foots the bill, even when private industry is allowed to reap the profits. Thus the means of control remain in official hands.

Here, as in the economic order, there has been an invasion of technologists at the decision-making level. Lawyers still far outnumber scientists in most branches of government. But increasingly they face problems that require the knowledge of the laboratory even if one can still apply the precedents to be found in the law libraries. The disciplines meet in such new creations as atomic energy commissions and space agencies, and the result is often confusion and conflict. One characteristic survives in these mixed bureaucracies: those trained to observe the laws of nature have no difficulty in embracing Parkinson's Law of expanding bureaucracy, and these new-style agencies proliferate like any other.

The magazine *Science* stated the dilemma bluntly:

> Since the legislative branch cannot evaluate technical proposals, the temptation arises to employ phony arguments in advocating major projects. In scientific circles there is a tendency to be more concerned with the glamorous saleable aspects of a proposal than with the intrinsic merits. Admitting more scientists to government posts would not help, for a) in becoming politicians they would in general lose their professional acuity before long, and b) it is doubtful whether a scientist would bring more wisdom to his job than would a lawyer.

The article notes that "some of the most narrow-minded, uncompromising, chauvinistic individuals in this world are scientists." To this one must add: and technologists.

Here the dichotomy between the scientist-technologist and the humanist reveals itself in its most fateful form. The most common response is to attack the problem through a reorganization of our educational institutions. Here, it is argued, is the place to train policymakers who, whether in a government office or as *Homo politicus* working in science and technology, can reach judgments that accommodate both technical factors and human ends.

In any event the size and number of functioning "political technologies" seems to be growing constantly. Their interrelation with the political order is by no means smooth and efficient even in governments with the most rigid systems of centralized control; in the U.S.S.R. the problem of holding this complex of scientific/technological operations together, assigning to each its place and set of priorities, and keeping all of them in balance, seems to be no less difficult than in the more open societies of the West. With or without a theoretical popular base, the authorizing mandates of these political technologies are necessarily becoming more and more general and in some cases they threaten to fade into practical insignificance. Even without recognizing Ellul's demon, it is possible to see a tendency in the political-technological combination to take on a gestalt of its own and to follow its own "laws."

Analogous problems are to be found in the slow growth of such supranational technological policymaking bodies as Euratom or the European Coal and Steel Community. These agencies tend to hide behind their supranational character when defending their autonomic policies. While presumably pioneering for a new unity among communities, they can without early detection become too rigidly bureaucratic to direct a policy adequately supporting general technological development, or conversely, they may be swayed unwittingly into some narrower nationalistic course. By their nature they are generally removed still one more step from popular control, with a council of foreign ministers providing only a tenuous link to the several electorates involved.

An electorate that is uninformed on the issues dealt with by political technologies is reduced to saying yes or no to broadly stated generalities. The natural tendency is to say yes to keep the system going so that we may continue to reap the presumed benefits of technological development. When the technological issue is presented in terms of survival, effective choice virtually disappears—as every nation has demonstrated in wartime.

There are those who profess to locate the root of the trouble in the irreversible fact that the technology is becoming more and more science-directed. They see the ultimate development of the technological order as a mathematical order, which converts all human activities into abstract and symbolic processes suitable for a computer, thus eliminating the old-fashioned personal and intuitive elements. If this in fact becomes a possibility all the existing orders would disappear, for society would have passed into 1984 and beyond, with Big Brother in charge of all our affairs.

The Social Component

From the moment the first roving tribes settled down to practise agriculture, man began to employ technology to shape his environment. This procsss interacted profoundly with the social order that developed concurrently with the technological order across the centuries. The quality of life for individual, family, and community was determined by the extent and the manner Nature was brought under man's control. In the ultimate development, factory-based industrialization—a technological datum—and urbanization—a sociological datum—are interacting in a similar way. If space exploration permits man to expand his environment beyond the earth he will take his social order with him and once again reshape it to the demands and possibilities of still another technological revolution.

The social order may be seen as a battlefield on which *Homo faber* has to compete with *Homo ludens, Homo politicus,* and *Homo economicus.* It is the focus of many conflicting needs and desires, arising from these different aspects of man. Primitive society held its few craftsmen in awe, and they often remained strangers to the community at large, feared because of their mysterious skills. Technologists are now generally ranked well down in the social pecking order, although their collective influence in shaping society may exceed that of any other group. *Homo faber* has always aimed at converting the unique into the ordinary, and in modern society he has become the great leveler, converting content into form, reason into routine, art into technique.

The structure of our social classes has been profoundly changed by the impact of technology. We are living in a world far removed from the Victorian Age. The Marxists have made a deliberate effort to employ the technological revolution as one of their means to the end of a classless society. This has led to a new stratification and differentiation, somewhat different from that anticipated by Marxian doctrine. In both East and West we have seen the rise of a new elite class, the "managers of society," whose power does not derive from traditional class sources and is likely to be transient and diffuse. These are the often anonymous decision-makers in the upper reaches of the huge public and private bureaucracies spawned by technology.

The very complexity of modern technology demands a higher degree of organization of our society, and one of a different kind. The spectacular ideological conflicts of the age are undoubtedly profoundly important, but they may have less long-range influence than the issues raised by the fact that in Western society the proportion of man-made to natural environment has effectively shifted past the mid-point. The evolution of megalopolis has destroyed qualities traditionally considered vital to the individual and the community. The physical manifestations may be seen in the extent of the rationalization and organization of daily life, the growth of standardization in goods and services, the vastly increased amount of information in circulation, and the rise of noise levels and congestion.

The consequences are the occasional breakdown of over-loaded services in great cities such as New York—and on the social side an increase of human tensions that frequently flare into full-scale riots. The modern city bears little resemblance to those where the ideals of urban civilization were first enunciated. No one could locate in Los Angeles, London, Amsterdam, or Moscow anything resembling the close-knit *polis* which characterized the ancient Greek city. Politicians of East and West still proclaim and appeal to the traditional "sense of community" but the soundings taken by sociologists indicate that it is steadily declining, despite—or perhaps because of—the modern means of communication technology has put at our disposal. Thus the phenomenon that sees the modern citizen reject the place of his livelihood and the centre of his culture; he regards it no longer as his city, but as an agglomeration he seeks to escape by spending as much of his time as possible in a cultivated demiwilderness called suburbia. The pattern of commuting once regarded as an American eccentricity has crossed the iron curtain; the highest reward for a Soviet bureaucrat is a *dacha* in the country and an automobile to take him back and forth to work.

Generally speaking, affluence seems to have isolated the individual from the community in which he lives. This may always have been true in the case of the wealthy few of previous times, but now technology has extended affluence to the majority, and alienation has become a mass phenomenon that exists in upper as well as lower classes. "*Homo Americanus* seems to be bored to death with his three-car garage," Clifton Fadiman has noted, "and juvenile delinquents now come in considerable part from middle-class and upper-class families."

At the other end of the scale there is an enforced leisure called unemployment. Ergonomists may be able to establish optimum teamwork between man and machine, but the social adaptation of surplus labour remains a major issue. We may adopt welfare-state techniques to meet the material needs of displaced workers and to maintain their purchasing power in the market; the continuing structural unemployment in the United States has brought on serious discussion of a guaranteed annual income without regard to work performed. But no one can doubt that in this situation we would face a vast new array of social and psychological problems.

The technologists have made it possible to predict a world in which the battle for raw materials needed to satisfy long-felt wants is finally won; leisure is plentiful; and the machine does all the hard or dull work. The price exacted so far for this emerging utopia has been the sacrifice of the worker's sense of belonging to a society that needs his strengths and skills. *Technologia* originally meant "giving rules to the arts"; the craftsman by a creative act shaped matter into forms he had conceived in his mind. Thus a harmony was achieved between the world of his mind, his spiritual world, and the work of his hands, the "manufacture" into which he put something of himself. For many, and perhaps for most in industrialized society, this essential quality survives only in the hobby to which they turn when they cannot discover any creative component in the work assigned them by an affluent society. And technology, having saddled the worker with boredom, through its advances in medicine and diet has prolonged the period he must endure it; the "old people" are a new social problem in every advanced country, where retirement comes about earlier and longevity is extended.

In these social areas, the technologist comes to the limits of his value-free order. He may, therefore, have a special concern when he sees social scientists apparently adapting his techniques and standards to research and programs involving human beings. It is not inconceivable that political leaders might seek to resolve their current dilemmas by transferring to sociology the manipulative controls now applied by technologists. This theoretically could produce a new, rapid acculturation which might remove the difficulties of accommodating traditional values of the individual, the family, and the community to the new, mechanized world we seem to be fated to build.

The World of Arts

The ring of man, machine, and milieu encircles the visible technological order, but it has always received its impulses from the world of the spirit. Many religions and many philosophies have inspired man to his technical achievements, and these have taken him past techniques to the arts as he sought to express the needs and wishes of his age. It is now commonly argued that technology has become a cultural leveler, threatening the arts with destruction and dividing the people into a cultural elite on the one hand and a mass of insensate culture consumers on the other. Yet in all the ages the world of the spirit has never been finally stifled by technological success. In the Greek world, technology was most advanced in the Athens of Pericles; Florence in the age of the Medici was an important industrial centre; and so was Paris in the days when the Académie Royale was founded. And the masses participated only to a limited extent and rather passively in those great cultures in which a small elite maintained the artists and shaped technology to their special demands.

Technology and the arts in fact are inseparable, although their practitioners have different domains. The artist works in the world of the spirit as he molds matter, creates images, or spins words and sounds into forms that delight those who receive them. The technologist remains in the world of Nature, reshaping matter and harnessing processes to meet the material wishes of his generation. Artists have been inspired by technological forms which often are projections of mathematical functions, and modern technology provides the means of diffusing much of their work. Mechanical means now provide the usual link between the painter, the musician, and the writer and the great bulk of his audience. If this process has been made possible the popularization that has debased some creative spirits, it has also brought the highest manifestations of culture to millions who enter what André Malraux has called a "museum without walls."

In a remarkable essay in the *Times Literary Supplement*, Marshall McLuhan points out that "from the neolithic age men had been engaged in creating technological extensions of their bodies in various fragmented and specialist forms, whether of script, or wheel, or housing, or money"; he concludes that a great breakthrough came with electricity and its impact on technology:

> The electronic age is distinct from any other age in having extended the human nervous system itself in a group of external technologies. The numerous extensions of hands and feet in the various forms of spindles and wheels and rods now begin to yield the circuit and the loop "where the hand of man never set foot." The immediate extensions of our nervous system by telegraph and telephone and radio and television not only usher us into a period when the codifying and moving of information supersede all other tasks in scope and in the creation of wealth, but they involve us totally in one another's lives. The extensions of our nerves and senses, as they constitute a new man-made environment, also require a wholly new kind of understanding of the sensory materials of this new environment and of the learning processes to which they are so deeply related.[4]

McLuhan holds that with Baudelaire art became coextensive with discovery and knowledge in every sphere of human activity, and quotes T. S. Eliot as having pointed out the effects of the internal combustion engine on poetic rhythm. He continues:

> Paradoxically, the acceleration of information movement restores to us the habit of mythical and inclusive perception . . . the electric circuit has restored to us the world of pattern recognition and to an understanding of the life of forms which had been denied to all but the artists of the now receding mechanical age. . . . The elimination of the job in the work process means a return to the depth involvement formerly associated only with arts and crafts. But now in the Age of Information the work

[4] "Culture and Technology," Aug. 6, 1964, p. 700.

> process and the learning process [process of creativity] become interfused. Automation is "learning a living." [5]

McLuhan believes that a concurrent revolution will take place in the world of learning where

> the extensions of our senses technologically should have a direct effect upon the sensory usage and preferences of any community. Many of these effects are quite incompatible with the continuance of older values. Once a sensory typology has been established for a given population, therefore, it is possible to predict the effect on that sensory typology of any given new artifact such as the motor car, or television. That is to say, it becomes possible to control or to avoid kinds of innovation that are destructive of such established values as we prefer to retain. A large measure of personal and social autonomy thus becomes possible across the entire spectrum of culture and technology, much in the way that we now have the means of thermostatic control of the thermal environment. A full understanding of the sensory typology of cultures on one hand, and the sensory order and impact of art and technology on the other hand, affords the possibility of a human environment sensorially programmed for the maximum use of the human powers of learning.[6]

Among the many theories on the relationship between the artist, the arts, the audience, and the world, those of McLuhan are as radical as any. Yet this advanced argument turns on the fact that the arts still preserve (mostly unconsciously) the memory of their once close contact with the crafts that developed into our often dehumanized technology. If the world of the spirit has survived even this assault by the machines, who can say that there may not yet be another great flowering of culture and the arts?

The Things of Value

Like any other field of human activity, technology can be said to be governed by its own rules and standards of value, but it can hardly claim a philosophy of its own. T

[5] Ibid, pp. 700–701.

[6] Ibid, p. 701.

large number of crafts which have merged into the modern technological order had a common way of thinking, and so they represented a unity of method and analysis that is paralleled in that of science. This pattern of thought, though profoundly rooted in Western culture, has been transferred with some success to every part of the world. However, it applies only to certain situations, to operations to effect certain changes in the environment which society in effect has commissioned the technologist to perform. It is in fact a pragmatic and utilitarian way of thinking, and the technologist must be aware of this fact that his "philosophy" has little value outside its own domain.

It might be argued that the contemporary philosophical systems designated as positivism and existentialism represent radically different reactions to the same inescapable set of technological facts. So, as noted above, does the philosophical theory embodied in Marxism. The mere recitation of this list indicates that impact of the technological age has not moved the philosophers any closer to the ultimate, universal answers they seek.

In its origins philosophy was concerned with many of the matters with which science and technology are concerned today. Early Greek philosophy sought to give a rational account of the origin and the existing state of the world and the powers operative within it. Logic and theory of knowledge developed as its instruments. Science thus evolved as a handmaiden to the philosopher, although he was less concerned with empirical inquiries about facts than with dialectical and analytical inquiries into meaning. Philosophy still adhered to the Platonic ideal of establishing a synoptic doctrine which led to the mastery of abstractions and yielded precepts of wisdom and of one's attitude in life.

Modern computerized technology and the sciences guiding it have not broken their ancient ties with certain aspects of philosophy. Indeed, technology has become more and more dependent upon mathematics, and the computer would not be possible without it. The engineer constantly handles such qualitative concepts as function, cause, mechanical order, and efficiency, which he tries to express in terms of quantity. This synthesis is inherent in the philosophy of mathematics (or theory of foundations). Based on the work of Pasch and Hilbert at the beginning of this century the theory of foundations soon extended beyond purely mathematical concepts and led to an inquiry into the nature of mathematical theories and the scope of mathematical methods. The discussions between Brouwer, Hilbert, and Heyting led to a formal system of intuitionist logic and mathematics and provided the background for the techniques of computerization. For this the problems of computability and decidability had to be solved. Post, and independently Turing, described a theoretical computing machine and its functioning as early as 1936. This was discussed and criticized by Church and Goedel. Other new branches of the philosophy of mathematics, such as symbolic logic (Kleene, Bethe, Tarski) provided other basic elements for the techniques of formulating or programming the questions to which the computer can provide intelligible answers. This has greatly advanced the clarification and classification of the uses to which servomechanisms and computers can be applied in the technological order.

If philosophy has not yet presented us with a single coherent view of the world on which all men can agree, there are a good many sectors of conceptual framework about which there is no serious disagreement. Further challenge seems inescapable, however, since technology now seems capable of merging the world of man with a world of ciphers, and of drowning the human spirit in an ocean of quantities.

For the Greek philosopher science was *theoria,* a part of natural philosophy; but now that science has struck an alliance with technology, it has moved away from *theoria* and become *praxis.* Thus many philosophers still turn away from those manifestations of the age they tend to consider a-cultural. It is more comfortable to view the development of technology as autonomic. The argument goes that the autonomy of Nature conveyed ideas which man used for his technical development. Technological achievements thus worked according to the way they were rooted in Nature. Human knowledge, the domain of the philosopher, on the other hand was abstract and experimental in character. But, while the development of technology advanced the experimental aspects of science, the technical means it created served, in turn, to promote man's quest for theoretical knowledge. The technological order thus must be considered as the extension of this experimental aspect of the whole of human culture, and inescapably it has forced its way onto the philosopher's agenda.

And of the Spirit

The world of religion transcends the immediately temporal; hence, its direct contacts with technology are negligible. But religions are differentiated by their attitude toward the conditions in which man lives, and not all of the world's great and enduring faiths can be said to be neutral or hostile to the technological order. The Buddhist is concerned with the annihilation of personality, and so the temporal conditions of technology can be of little interest to him; one of the first commandments of Buddhism is the renunciation of all ties with matter. Confucianism developed as the religion of a society of landlords and peasants, in which technology was given no place of importance. But the Christian religion fashioned its tenets in such a way as to forge an inescapable link with the man-made world.

Modern technology was born in the Middle Ages in the Christian West. Its moving spirit is imbued with Christian ideas, notably the recognition of the inherent worth of the individual, and the belief that the forces of Nature are not spiritual but material and are destined to be used by mankind. These tenets of the faith penetrated the whole of Western culture, far beyond the limits of the organized Churches, and they have survived the diminishing influence of religion in a skeptical age. Many of the difficulties encountered in the export of the West's advanced technology to other parts of the world are rooted in the differences in religious attitude, and our urge to extend the material blessings of our advanced systems in part at least is a response to the basic humanitarian creed of Christianity.

The attitude of the Christian churches toward science and technology has been complex and contradictory. All men were placed under the curse of Adam: "In the sweat of thy face shalt thou eat bread" (Genesis 3:19), and no technological act is supposed to undo the consequences of the curse. The Church in fact developed an early tradition of deep distrust toward the scientist, who challenged the verities, and the technologist, who profaned Nature. This hostility was a powerful force in the Middle Ages, and through the tenets of the Counter-Reformation it survived far into modern times, producing persecutions and absurdities along the way.

But the same Bible that records God's curse on Adam contains the passages that became the foundation of a quite different attitude toward science and spurred technology on to the mastery of Nature. The Lord, according to Genesis 1:26 and Psalms 8:4–8, gave man authority over the "things in the earth." Man was not only created in such a way that he was capable of controlling his environment, he was *intended* to control it—in a responsible fashion, of course, for which he would be judged when he appeared before God's tribunal.

Roger Bacon informed Pope Clement IV that science should be steered toward making Christianity fit to compete intellectually and morally with pagans and infidels. Ramon Llull suggested that scientific enlightenment should be encouraged, because once the mind of man had been opened by science, his conversion to Christianity was inevitable. At the end of the 14th century John of Rupescissa remarked that a philosopher should first purify his mind by a devout life and profound contemplation in order to recognize Nature for what it is and learn how to change what can be changed.

So the argument went. With their greater emphasis on the concept of grace on the one hand and predestination on the other, the Protestant sects tended to let technological development take its course. They have rarely condemned it, as such, although their social gospels have sent some denominations into the lists against its inhuman manifestations.

In recent decades the Catholic Church has made remarkable efforts to find a common denominator for faith and knowledge on which to reconcile religion, science, and technology. The great Ecumenical Council, Vatican II, gave a powerful impulse to this tendency, and among the prime initiators was a great scientist of the Church, Pierre Teilhard de Chardin. Joseph Cardinal Frings of Cologne has compared technology, which today is conquering and unifying the world, to the *koine*, the language universally understood during the earliest days of Christianity: "The Church today finds herself face to face with a new kind of *koine*, that is, a universal way of thinking and speaking. This *koine* is the product of the progress of technology which is valid across all frontiers and iron curtains." Another Catholic scholar, Jean Daniélou, S.J., said "Nothing is more biblical than technology." C. F. D. Moule of Cambridge in his 1964 Ethel M. Wood lecture set forth a "Biblical Ecology":

> [St. Paul explains (Rom. viii) how creation was subjected to frustration when Adam's sin pulled down nature with it.] . . . restoration and liberation come when man assumes his proper position in ecology, not contracting out of his responsibilities and giving up the use of nature, but using it responsibly and according to the will of God . . . The emancipation of nature from its servitude to decay consists . . . in its material still being used . . . in an overall purpose that is part of God's design. Man's responsibility is not to refrain from using material: it is for him to use it responsibly, both within his body and outside it.[7]

The qualities the medieval philosopher demanded in a good scientist have always been rare, and they still are. But in the face of temptation and torture there have been notable refusals to abdicate moral responsibility. Leonardo da Vinci would not divulge the secret of the submarine he had designed, as he says in his *Notebooks*, "on account of the evil nature of men who would practice assassination at the bottom of the seas." For similar reasons Boyle kept the secret of a poison he had made in the laboratory, and Napier of a weapon he had designed. Tartaglia, the Italian mathematician, worked out a theory on the trajectory of projectiles which would have been invaluable to artillery commanders, but he tore up the manuscript and rewrote it many years later only after the Turks had invaded his native country. Faraday is known to have refused to work out a formula for a poison gas to be used in the Crimean War.

The current generation of scientists and technologists face similar moral decisions in the research and manufacture of nuclear weaponry and delivery systems. Ronald W.

[7] *Man and Nature in the New Testament,* The Athlone Press, London, 1964, pp. 11, 14–15.

Clark remarked, "A scientist is always asking himself: 'Am I on the right track? but the men making the bomb had to face another question in almost the same words: 'Am I doing right?' " Neither the public argument over this question, nor the internal debate conducted by many contemporary scientists and technologists, can be said to have been settled in any of the great powers or in the smaller nations that seek admission to the "nuclear club." Many, however, are at least committed to the proposition voiced by Niels Bohr, who said of the first nuclear experiments, the vital thing was not to make the bomb work, but to consider, before it was too late, how to control its use if it did work.

It has been proposed that there should be a Hippocratic Oath for the technologist as there is for the physician. But the answer is not in such formal trappings, but in the inner faith of the men who make the basic inventions—and of those in all the orders of modern life who must share the responsibility if *Homo faber's* genius is finally turned against himself.

Envoy

The Indians on the west coast of South America tell a folk tale which must be very old, since the scene it describes is depicted on a pre-Chimu pottery vase some 1400 years old. The story runs as follows:

This has happened and it will happen again. Long, long ago the sun disappeared and the world was shrouded in complete darkness for five long days. This was the signal for the things to mobilize. The stones began to grind, the mortars and pestles marched against their masters, and even the llamas attacked their keepers in the stables.

In our time there is a tendency to catch sight of that same frightening vision—to blame our tools for showing malice because our world has gone wrong in so many ways. It is tempting to sit in the midst of the strange and wonderful array of our modern technology and cry out with the sorcerer's apprentice: "How can I get rid of the spirits I have called up myself?" The question is whether we, who have dominion over the earth, shall act like Sisyphus and trust to our cunning only, becoming more and more self-reliant and self-involved, self-imprisoned and self-centred. Sisyphus became his own God and his own

Satan, at war with heaven, embittered with earth, and contemptuous of hell. But this author, after contemplating three-quarters of a century of technology's marvels and horrors, has no doubt that Sisyphus has already been saved from himself. This happened at Easter.

Index